Daily Telegraph

BIG BOOK OF QUICK CROSSWORDS 3

Daily Telegraph

BIG BOOK OF QUICK CROSSWORDS 3

Published by Telegraph Publications
135 Fleet Street, London EC4P 4BL

First published 1986

ISBN 0 86367 099 7

Typeset by Wordsmiths Graphics Ltd, Street, Somerset
Printed in Great Britain by St Edmundsbury Press, Bury St Edmunds

THE PUZZLES

1

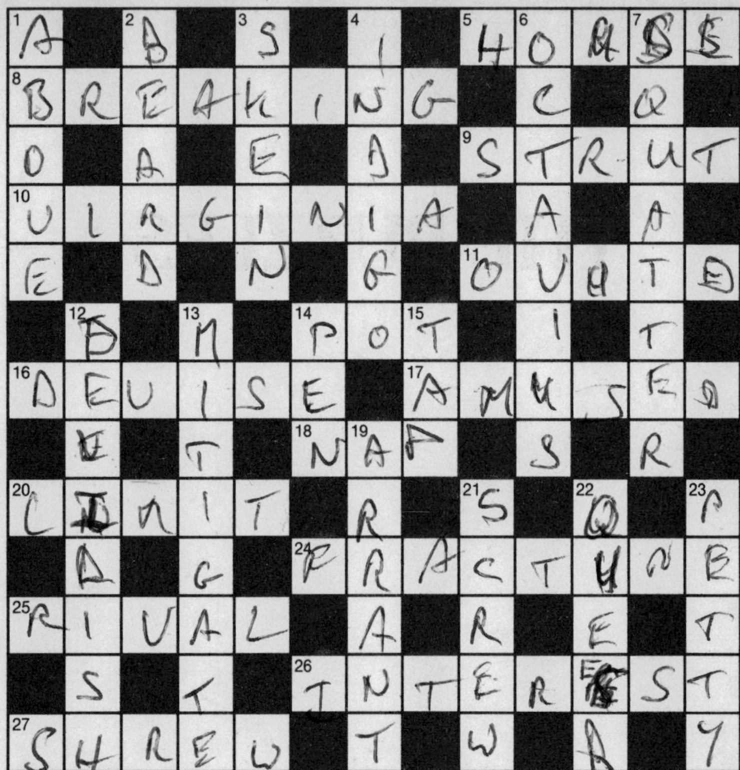

ACROSS

5 Parliamentary chamber
8 Training a colt
9 Walk pompously
10 American state
11 Egg-shaped
14 Sink snooker ball
16 Invent
17 Entertained
18 Small sleep
20 Permissible extent
24 Breakage
25 Competitor
26 Return on investment
27 Bad-tempered woman

DOWN

1 Over
2 Facial hair
3 Loop of wool
4 Dark blue
6 The young Augustus
7 He takes unauthorised possession of empty house
12 Wickedly cunning
13 Alleviate
14 Female swan
15 Hit gently
19 Downright
21 Propeller
22 Peculiar
23 Insignificant

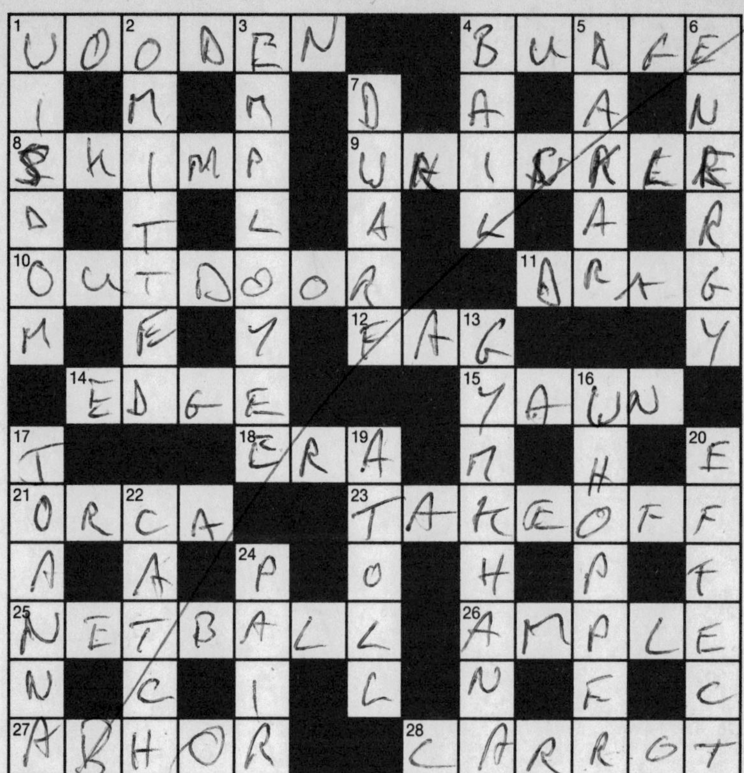

ACROSS
1 Dull, insensible
4 Move or stir
8 Stint
9 Valuable hint
10 In the open air
11 To trail
12 Drudgery
14 Brink
15 Gape
18 Age
21 Killer whale
23 Start of flight (4,3)
25 Team sport on court
26 Abundant
27 Loathe
28 Root veg

DOWN
1 Sagacity
2 Left out
3 Paid worker
4 Security for the accused
5 Senegal capital
6 Vigour
7 Diminutive man
13 Equestrian sports meeting
16 Monstrous lie
17 Girl's name
19 Lagoon's coral reef
20 Bring about
22 Ensnare
24 Arrange in twos

3

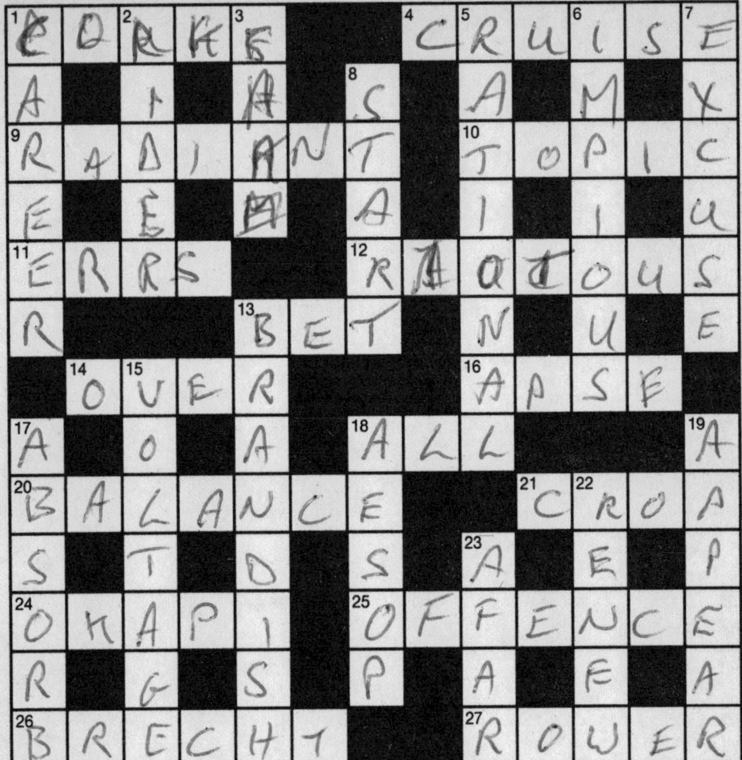

ACROSS
1 Stoppers
4 Pleasure voyage
9 Shining
10 Theme
11 Sins
12 Noisy and disorderly
13 Wager
14 Finished
16 Church recess
18 Everyone
20 Equilibrium
21 Hunting whip
24 Giraffe-like animal
25 Umbrage
26 German dramatist
27 Oarsman

DOWN
1 Profession
2 Corollary
3 Bogus
5 Sane
6 Irreverent
7 Pretext
8 Commence
13 Flourish
15 Electromotive force
17 Swallow up
18 Greek fabulist
19 Seem
22 Renovate
23 At a distance

ACROSS

1 One of the United States
4 Lessees
8 Nut
9 Worth
10 Toilet requisite
11 At home
13 Hawk around
15 Decayed
17 Afternoon rest
20 Felines
22 Young dogs
24 Command
26 Recess
27 Envisage
28 Christmas blazer (4,3)
29 50-50 chance

DOWN

1 Woolly scarf
2 Ice hut
3 Lift up
4 Tasty morsel
5 Wanderer
6 On edge
7 Areas for building
12 Cosy dwelling
14 At one time
16 Coal pit (anag.)
18 Set apart
19 Stuffy
21 Questioning
22 Small coin
23 Couldn't be better
25 Golf shot

5

ACROSS

1 Tangles in string
4 Song to greet the dawn
9 Disease transmitted by mosquitoes
10 Spherical
11 Back of the neck
12 Hopelessness
13 Fling, toss
14 Ring of light
16 Want
18 Students' festival
20 Pupil, ward
21 U.S. State
24 Gross, stupid
25 Suspicion of injury, offence
26 Blotchy
27 Foe

DOWN

1 Japanese robe
2 Ship's lowest deck
3 Channel Island
5 Rebellion
6 Fawn upon, flatter
7 Tolerate
8 Accessible
13 English county
15 Alligator pear
17 Small spots
18 Picture-puzzle
19 Good-humoured
22 Vestige
23 Wind instrument

6

ACROSS
5 Sedate
8 United
9 Gauzy
10 Witty retort
11 Pool
14 Pig-pen
16 Yacht station
17 Stick
18 Male cat
20 Service award
24 Quarters for soldiers
25 Condescend
26 Highland broadsword
27 Viper

DOWN
1 Downright
2 Open-mouthed
3 Begin
4 Iterate
6 Dusk
7 Unripe
12 Gifted
13 Child's apron
14 Posed
15 Sweet-potato
19 ITV teletext service
21 Entreats
22 Small shovel
23 Doorkeeper

7

ACROSS

1 Young swan
4 Herts town
8 Contemptible person
9 Gourd fruit
10 Discountenanced
11 Object of worship
12 Objective
14 Avoid
15 Reflected sound
18 Liquid refreshment
21 Spheres
23 Scurry
25 Barred
26 Futile
27 Man-made fibre
28 Heavy and claggy

DOWN

1 Seize (sl.)
2 Hungarian stew
3 Large animal
4 Big volume
5 Needled
6 Bait maggot
7 Bone-ash porcelain
13 Falling in ruins
16 Impetuous person
17 Alarm-bell
19 Stage whisper
20 Considerable
22 Precious crystal stone
24 Twirl

ACROSS
1 Citrus fruits
5 Annul
8 Restrict
9 Disparate
10 Laid bare
11 Abhorred
12 Edict
14 Ailment
17 Traverse
19 One more
22 Moment
23 Dispossess by law
24 Attempt
25 Continued

DOWN
1 Lubricated
2 Calendar
3 Confined to college
4 Robust
5 Peruvian Indian
6 Grown-up
7 Vacation
12 Cheat
13 Rapture
15 Godlessness
16 Chaff
18 Fertile spot in desert
20 Unlocks
21 Scolded

9

ACROSS
1 Flag
7 Herb
8 Clarify
9 Peculiar
10 Thunder god
11 Ordinary
13 Sheep's coat
14 Foolish
17 Clever
18 Vocal
20 Cinque port
22 Capable
23 Period of time
24 Climbing plant

DOWN
1 Sugary
2 Fashionable (1,2,4)
3 Entrance
4 Cause
5 Romantic poet
6 Hawked
7 White ant
12 Damage slightly
13 Blacksmith
15 Ideal
16 Brutish creature
17 Underneath
19 Water-lily
21 Sports side

ACROSS
7 Beasts of pasture
8 Lumberjack
10 On end, virtuous
11 General tendency
12 Confront
13 Dumpy
17 Gathering of witches
18 Cavil
22 Slow, mournful song
23 Acrobat
24 Head-cushion
25 Japanese robe

DOWN
1 Untidy
2 Pull
3 Make parallel
4 Highwayman
5 White heron
6 Company of lions
9 Rules of politeness
14 Tedium
15 Language of Belgium
16 Common bird
19 Proficient
20 Crimped edging
21 Circuit, precincts

11

ACROSS
1 Bandit
4 Unfruitful
7 Sweet scent
9 Daring
10 Way out
11 Gulled
13 Rue
14 Scrivener
15 Gain
17 Pollute
19 Citrus fruit
20 Solid fat
22 Prosecuted
23 Cheat
24 Guard
25 Scolding

DOWN
1 Eraser
2 Flier
3 Stew
4 Defeated
5 Track event
6 Tidily
7 Small flute
8 King Arthur's sword
11 Evil spirit
12 Senior diplomat
15 Sign of the zodiac
16 Irritable
17 Water-diviner
18 Termination
21 Go jogging
22 Dispatched

ACROSS
1 Salad vegetable
5 Jump in fright
8 Question at length
9 Wooden plate
10 Window cover
11 Telegraphic code
12 Avaricious
14 Needed quickly
17 Insurgent
19 Joined the gap
22 Jungle cat
23 In angry mood
24 Fear greatly
25 Omission of duty

DOWN
1 Capital of Nigeria
2 Speech of recognition
3 Not illuminated
4 Vast realm
5 Speech impediment
6 Michaelmas daisy
7 Treat cruelly
12 Verbally hashed
13 Dunce
15 Scratch design
16 Iranian port
18 Penniless
20 Sugar-topping
21 Lived

13

ACROSS	
1	Magistrate
5	Counter-balance
8	Urge forward
9	Diluted
10	Effective
12	Dove sound
13	Merriment
14	Open the wine
17	Plant
18	In unruly fashion
20	Vertical
21	French river
23	Sea-duck
24	Jostled

DOWN	
1	Fruit liquid
2	Small liquid mouthful
3	Unlicensed
4	High estimation
5	Card game
6	Harmless
7	Sea-fish
11	Squandered piecemeal
13	Meaningful movement
15	Provokes
16	A whisk
18	Light beer
19	Concede
22	Unwell

14

ACROSS

1 Blood-vessel
3 Splendid
9 Uptight
10 Denied
11 Rim
13 Reduce to powder
14 Gratify
16 Estimate
18 Rubbing
20 Stitch
22 Temporary habitation
23 Turf
25 Taken ill
26 Shortly

DOWN

1 Essential
2 Hostelry
4 Solitary
5 Rues
6 Non-members
7 Sorrow
8 Pile
12 Prevents
14 Widely favoured
15 Sitting
17 Mix
19 Pant
21 Enlarge
24 Fuss

15

ACROSS

1 Discern by smell
4 Crowding in
8 Endeavour
9 Follow
10 Big
11 Beer mug
13 Stride
15 Love-apple
17 Church festival
20 Quotation
22 Military leader
24 Illumination
26 Colouring medium
27 Deer meat
28 Underground prison
29 Residence

DOWN

1 Small onion
2 Penetrate
3 Violent storm
4 Tiny and neat
5 Spotless
6 Moment
7 Avarice
12 Summit
14 Betting machine (abbr.)
16 Very great number
18 Capital of Georgia
19 Train
21 Soccer team
22 Roman god of love
23 Inter (anag.)
25 Zest

ACROSS
1 Pitman
4 Wharfs
10 Residential area of London
11 Capsize
12 Courtyard
13 Speech impediment
15 Blood-sucking insect
17 Foolishly giddy
19 Constrict windpipe
22 Chide, scold
25 Low wall along edge of roof, etc
27 Cook by dry heat
29 Provide with source of income
30 Food
31 Bizarre
32 Gemstone

DOWN
2 Sluggish
3 Lessen strain (4,3)
5 Fleshy pendent in throat
6 Muslim face-veil
7 Range of view
8 Moral fall
9 Wading bird
14 Diplomacy
16 Ancient stringed instrument
18 Condense written work
20 Fish
21 Velocity
23 Book of maps
24 Speak out
26 Military potential
28 Watchful

17

ACROSS

1 Cut with clippers
4 Torment
8 Crack
9 Subject
10 Proportion
11 Unobtrusiveness
13 Mormon state
15 Death
17 Welsh wizard
20 Endure
22 Attack
24 Surrey racecourse
26 Rapid
27 Base
28 Forebode
29 Entices

DOWN

1 Fastened
2 Choose
3 Disastrous
4 Girl's name
5 Considered
6 Useful implement or vessel
7 Foe
12 Resistance units
14 Relate
16 Huge
18 Everlasting
19 O.T. book
21 Clothing
22 Greek fabulist
23 Extreme
25 Abstemious

18

ACROSS

7 Financial gain
8 Edge
10 Cattle thief
11 Living
12 Composer of Rule Britannia
13 Ice-house
17 Oriental country
18 Rend
22 Speak
23 Foreign settler
24 Crop gatherer
25 Adjournment

DOWN

1 Enemy of Athens
2 Agree
3 Young mare
4 Outstanding example
5 Once more
6 Rage
9 Itinerary
14 Hare hound
15 Told
16 U.K. nationality
19 Liquid measure
20 Valuable violin (abbr.)
21 Urged

19

ACROSS

1 Shattering
7 Fragrant shrub
8 Garbage-monger
9 Rower's propeller
10 Put down
11 Pollen producer
13 Mendicant
14 Calm
17 Rumpled (as a bed)
18 Against
20 Cloth's woolly surface
22 State of deprivation
23 Occurrence
24 Grammatic construction

DOWN

1 Agave fibre
2 Causing wonder
3 Hastened
4 Nullify
5 Power-cable support
6 Cheat
7 Quiver
12 Article of clothing
13 Bed covering
15 Anxiety
16 Remain attached
17 Higher
19 Outflow
21 To coin

ACROSS

1 Manufacturer
4 Benefice
9 Frail
10 Spiked flower
11 Greek letter
12 Widespread
13 Enemy
14 Tumble
16 Healthy
18 Bishopric
20 Overseer
21 Festivity
24 Split
25 Greek currency
26 Cowardly
27 Irritable

DOWN

1 Toasted teacake
2 Deadly Indian snake
3 Collapse
5 Savoy opera
6 Endanger
7 Mild
8 Amalgamate
13 Long-legged bird
15 Coming
17 Brawl
18 Obliquely malicious
19 Illness
22 Remains
23 Treaty

21

ACROSS
- **1** Distinguished title
- **4** Taunt
- **8** Bird
- **9** Parcel
- **10** Matching jumper and cardigan (4-3)
- **11** Self-satisfied
- **12** Droop
- **14** Shaft of light
- **15** Associate
- **18** Newt
- **21** Elevate
- **23** Can be heard
- **25** Bounce back
- **26** Care for
- **27** Midlands river
- **28** Type of dancing

DOWN
- **1** Japanese sport
- **2** Account
- **3** Good-looking
- **4** Diplomacy
- **5** Danger signal
- **6** Vitality
- **7** Short gaiters
- **13** A reading (anag.)
- **16** Unstinting
- **17** Dark red wine
- **19** Late
- **20** Arid region
- **22** Myth
- **24** Fair

ACROSS

1 Gramophone record
3 Billiard-table rims
9 Marriage
10 Cooking area
11 Slash, tear open
13 Crowd, confluence
14 Scarcity
16 Flight of steps
18 Aim, objective
20 Terminate
22 Chief port of Libya
23 Considerable wealth
25 Official list, regularly kept
26 Buttress

DOWN

1 Raise objections
2 Coagulate
4 Cruel
5 In haste
6 Else
7 Virtuous, unblemished
8 Style, elegance
12 Toy
14 Aimless person
15 Slender, flimsy
17 Having a limit
19 Powerless to feel
21 Dark-coloured
24 Industrious insect

23

ACROSS
7 Seemly
8 Male goose
10 Remainder
11 Evict
12 Interval of calm
13 Laughter
17 Pick-me-up
18 Tiller
22 Gaping hollow
23 Parvenu
24 Affectionate
25 Flaw

DOWN
1 Glitter
2 Comfort
3 Prepared
4 Reddish purple
5 Modify
6 Ruff
9 O.T. book
14 Remark
15 Traduced
16 Ape
19 Climb
20 Ointment
21 Willow

24

ACROSS

1 Fielding position
4 Cavalry attack
9 Make better
10 One doomed to die
11 Knob
12 Pipe insulation
13 Primate animal
14 Open tart
16 Harbour vessels
18 Billiard stick
20 Sycophant
21 Parasite
24 Desert pool
25 Type of cloth
26 From Denmark
27 Rob

DOWN

1 Customer
2 Insipid
3 Civic disturbance
5 North London suburb
6 Talking bombastically
7 Make angry
8 Very pretty girl
13 A break-down
15 Exchange of information
17 Agreement
18 Royal headgear
19 Composer of The Messiah
22 Turning-tool
23 Weaponry

25

ACROSS

1 Angry
4 Buzzed round
8 Raise
9 Deduce
10 Opposite to inner
11 Enormous
13 Unctuous
15 Tossed
17 Haphazard
20 Stuff
22 White lady?
24 Grotesque
26 Plea of absence
27 Braced framework
28 Fell
29 American stock-farm

DOWN

1 Blunt cigar
2 Open
3 Small bird
4 Insect in stored grain
5 Mode of language
6 Purified
7 Funeral hymn
12 Mary (anag.)
14 Move by slow degrees
16 Practical viewpoint
18 Non-professional
19 Shakespearean tragedy
21 Had a break
22 Forcible air-stream
23 Bad cold
25 Giant

ACROSS

1 Pig
4 Tried judicially
10 Expressive movement of body
11 Sweetener
12 Bloodsucker
13 Wilfully disregarded
15 Mah-jongg piece
17 Remains
19 Bottomless gulf
22 Learning
25 Climbing plant
27 Culpability
29 Insurgent
30 Enliven
31 Hinder, put off
32 Concur

DOWN

2 Barren region
3 Ill-behaved
5 Ruhr steel centre
6 Compliments
7 Nimble
8 Danger
9 Haughtiness
14 Tackle
16 Lies (anag.)
18 Quiver
20 Beseeching
21 Twenty
23 Keyboard instrument
24 Precipitous
26 Rhythmic throbbing
28 Angry

27

ACROSS

1 Choke
7 Sank a putt
8 Tiredness
9 Faint
10 Extinct bird
11 Young salmon
13 Boil with anger
14 Receive willingly
17 Sparing
18 Chinese vessel
20 Sheep
22 Mouth-organ
23 Seashore
24 Frenzied rush

DOWN

1 Firm
2 Remainder
3 Mr — Kinnock
4 Paris gallery
5 Cutting edge
6 Unyielding
7 Poisonous plant
12 Contemplated
13 Elongate
15 Learned
16 Mimic
17 Untamed
19 Court card
21 Space

28

ACROSS
1 Devastation
4 Snobbish (coll.)
9 Anchorage
10 Kind of bay window
11 Clutch
12 Violent wind-storm
13 Menagerie
14 Lies (anag.)
16 Pace
18 Donkey
20 Compressed, restricted
21 Large gull
24 French composer
25 Contemptuous of sacred things
26 Thrashing
27 Potentate

DOWN
1 Adoration
2 Stringed instrument
3 Edible mollusc
5 Headway
6 Mimic
7 Colour
8 Slow (mus.)
13 Airship
15 Deprived of food
17 Slight burn
18 Skilful
19 Progress through life
22 African hut-village
23 Needy

29

ACROSS
5 Aircraft
8 Cover
9 Perfume
10 Sparkles
11 Welcome
14 Strange
16 Convivial
17 Painter
18 Faint
20 Exclude
24 Determined
25 Condition
26 Strainer
27 Decorate

DOWN
1 Brink
2 Shun
3 Sluggishness
4 Unpunished
6 Tear
7 Balderdash
12 Unwarrantably interfered with
13 Calamity
14 Aged
15 Water barrier
19 Refrigerator
21 Hungarian wine
22 Surpass
23 Eerie

ACROSS

1 Head harness
4 Sugary
8 Helicopter blade
9 Spiritless
10 Swiss cheese
11 Slight
12 Knot together
14 Military dining room
15 Over-satisfy
18 Tree
21 Pointed doorway
23 Fatty
25 Regular drinker
26 Approximately
27 Push with elbow
28 Shooting star

DOWN

1 Salad vegetable
2 Enter uninvited
3 Generosity
4 Submerge
5 On a par
6 Henry VII to Elizabeth I
7 Fast
13 Considered guess
16 Pair
17 Large box
19 Wed
20 Trusted adviser
22 Managed
24 Adhesive

31

ACROSS
1 Puzzle compiler
4 Made weary, whispering sound
7 Head of State
9 Threatening
10 Blast of wind
11 Fish akin to turbot
13 Every 60 mins
14 Merited
15 Paining continuously
17 Deliver sermon
19 Every 24 hours
20 Black-leg
22 Blemish
23 Dirigible
24 Small canine pet (3-3)
25 Made things orderly

DOWN
1 Detective
2 Conservative
3 Devotional beads
4 A col
5 Hammer-bell
6 Marked with small spots
7 Hump along (anag.)
8 Part of record player
11 Suave
12 Lawrence (dim.)
15 Attack
16 Gambling
17 Flexible
18 Enmity
21 Celtic poet
22 Extorted from

32

ACROSS
1 Cabbage
3 Deficiency
9 Player
10 Council of ministers
11 Extinct bird
13 Welsh liquor made from honey
14 Pressed
16 Estimate
18 Random
20 Spinning toy
22 Worshipping
23 Automaton
25 Diminished
26 Salver

DOWN
1 Amulet
2 Destiny
4 Goddess of witches
5 Galoshes (U.S.)
6 Cancellation
7 Prolongs
8 Relentless
12 Shapeless
14 Biblical outcast
15 Inspect
17 Wringer
19 Venture
21 Trivial
24 Addition to medal

33

ACROSS

1 Cry plaintively
4 Spectacles
8 Syncopated jazz
9 Style of address
10 Liquid measure
11 Recount
13 Cosy home
15 Uncommon thing
17 Bandit
20 Deciduous trees
22 Meet head-on
24 Additional
26 Accumulate
27 This leg (anag.)
28 Design
29 Wander

DOWN

1 Songbird
2 Bar of metal
3 Obvious
4 Vegetables
5 Change
6 Go to sea (3,4)
7 Setting
12 Minute fragment
14 Looked at
16 Dependable
18 Ineffectual
19 Opulent
21 Period of instruction
22 Fastener
23 Publish
25 Striped feline

ACROSS

1 Coin
4 Characteristics
9 Uniform, steady
10 Sweetener
11 School room furniture
12 Tract of land
13 Volcanic dust
14 Contemptible person
16 Water jug
18 Assistance
20 Loud-voiced person
21 Small bird
24 Conveniently near
25 Preliminary draft
26 Repeat from memory
27 Port of N.W. Belgium

DOWN

1 Display
2 Drink
3 American University
5 Reticent
6 Thankless person
7 Malayan garment
8 Veracity
13 Purple gemstone
15 Cocaine (anag.)
17 O.T. Book
18 Inert gas
19 Turn upside down
22 European river
23 Male deer

35

ACROSS

1 Auctioneer's mallet
4 Farrier
8 Inferior
9 Lessened
10 Descriptive term
11 Kind
12 Headgear
14 Woden
15 Boulder
18 Sunburn
21 Swirl
23 Dishonourable
25 Egoistic
26 Cancel
27 Regal
28 Opposite of 8

DOWN

1 Small cable
2 Wed
3 Large pachyderm
4 Team
5 Prurient
6 Concealed
7 Thin soup
13 Cut short
16 Show-case
17 Hot spring
19 Darkness
20 Trader
22 Dawdle
24 Cultivate

ACROSS

1 Religious building
4 Cooking pear
7 Pirate
9 Become exhausted
10 Act
11 Evil spirit
13 Cad
14 Gazed lecherously
15 Very hot
17 Pious speech
19 Drunkard
20 Greek letter
22 Unexpected hitch
23 Worn out
24 Remove from text
25 Pinched

DOWN

1 Sailing vessel
2 Theatrical part
3 Seeker of game
4 Grain pest
5 Marsh plant
6 Required
7 A past tense
8 Admonish
11 Charge against account
12 Control rod
15 Placed before committee
16 Give
17 Add salt
18 Complained ceaselessly
21 Wheel rod
22 Soak through

37

ACROSS
7 Mohammedan place of worship
8 Consumers
10 Duplicate
11 Pawnbroker (sl.)
12 Den
13 Unrelenting
17 Tartan cloth
18 Mutilate
22 Ignite
23 Skilled physical exerciser
24 Ember
25 Golden yellow bird

DOWN
1 Green beryl
2 Preventing decay
3 Of ancient Carthage
4 The month of Janus
5 Wood barrier
6 Trembling poplar
9 A game-bird
14 Small speculation
15 Bullfighter
16 Left out
19 Spot or speckle
20 He acts for another
21 Smug smile

ACROSS

1 Deputy (5-2)
5 Stableman
8 Requisition
9 Small boring tool
10 Lured
11 Correct
12 Doorkeeper
14 Short-sighted
17 Acquiesce
19 Suitability
22 Nuclear missile
23 Vigilant
24 Plume
25 Large lizard

DOWN

1 Gradient
2 Listener
3 First Greek 8
4 Insignificant person
5 Barn
6 Egg-shaped
7 Tuneful
12 Synthetic polymer
13 Highest mountain
15 Gift
16 Small fowl
18 Uplift
20 Retinue
21 Woodland god

39

ACROSS

1 Habitual tobacco user
4 Ridicule
8 Snow leopard
9 Hoodlum
10 Abode
11 Lake
12 Large deer
14 Continent
15 Verdi opera
18 Permit
21 Move very slowly
23 A garble (anag.)
25 Draw out
26 Hurried
27 Woollen cloth
28 Truthful

DOWN

1 Pacify
2 Public transport
3 Net value (anag.)
4 Out of danger
5 Yellow-green colour
6 Herb
7 Packing container
13 Marsupial
16 Complete collapse
17 Gastropod
19 Dance
20 Brigand
22 Selected
24 Noisy

40

ACROSS
1 Zeal
5 Henry —, English sculptor
8 Heavenly body
9 Receptacle for coal
10 Autograph
12 Swine
13 Gallows
14 Preserve in vinegar
17 Mesh
18 Insolent disrespect
20 Ship's waiter
21 Of the moon
23 Radiating good humour
24 Isle in Thames estuary

DOWN
1 Confronts
2 Intoxicating spirit
3 Atrocious act
4 Bring from danger
5 Small rodent
6 Frank of speech
7 Space on reverse of coin, showing date, etc
11 Intermediary (2-7)
13 Creation
15 Gratify
16 Playing-cards suit
18 Republic in Europe
19 In good time
22 Casual sleep

41

ACROSS
1 Cost of journey
3 Barter
9 Private coach
10 Akin
11 Traveller's diary
13 Defeat
14 Roman emperor
16 Deleted
18 Outspokenness
20 Observed
22 Gather
23 Water-lily
25 International games
26 French cheese

DOWN
1 Deadly
2 Rodent
4 King of Persia
5 Pistol-case
6 Nudists
7 Given permanent income
8 Jason's ship
12 Little by little
14 Narcotic plant
15 Belgian port
17 Glasgow football team
19 Auction
21 Spend unprofitably
24 Sailor

ACROSS

1 Not hidden
4 Got money for work
9 Of immense size
10 Coarse fabric
11 Standard
12 Unblemished
13 Digit
14 Employer
16 Highest point
18 Frying vessel
20 Everlasting
21 Operatic song
24 Stiff broom
25 Warn
26 Indicate
27 Putting area

DOWN

1 Excursion
2 Go in
3 Pale colour
5 Senior councillor
6 Artless innocence
7 Weaken liquid
8 Extent
13 Pass on
15 Child of spouse
17 With toe membranes
18 Courage
19 Large gun
22 Lift up
23 Breathing organ

43

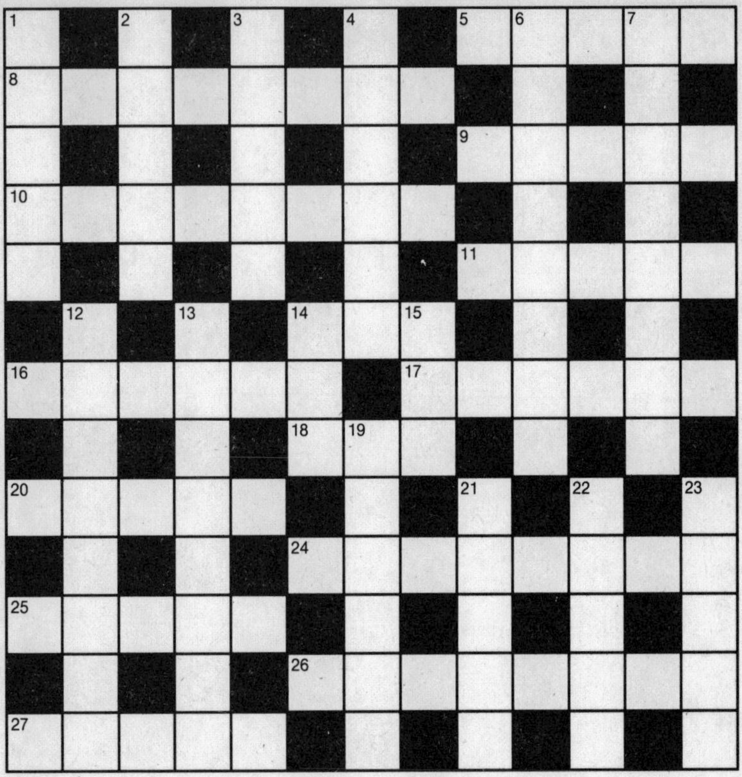

ACROSS
5 Whimper plaintively
8 Trader
9 Nurse — Cavell
10 Scum of the people (4-4)
11 Dutch ceramic-ware
14 Put on
16 Stroke
17 Disturber of peace
18 Work steadily
20 Sprinkle
24 Pert
25 Bishop's head-dress
26 Belittled
27 Intoxicating

DOWN
1 Smile smugly
2 Skilled trade
3 Extortioner
4 Stabbed
6 Prickly creature
7 Gave information of
12 Precious blue stone
13 Excluded
14 Reptile
15 Dehydrated
19 Sawed timber
21 Blaspheme
22 Reddish pigment or dye
23 Scrutinise

ACROSS
1 Spirit
4 Shallow dish
8 Garret
9 Ascetic
10 Expand
11 Weathercock
12 Outfit
14 Chafe
15 Anger
18 Spike of corn
21 Midwest state
23 Experience
25 Husbandry
26 Cape antelope
27 Giddy
28 Remained

DOWN
1 Grumbled
2 Nominal
3 Tear
4 Mail
5 Scene of combat
6 Oxford college
7 Bet
13 Slope
16 Divided country
17 Talented
19 Monarch
20 Squalid
22 Graceful dance
24 Misty

45

ACROSS

7 Constructing
8 Greek island
10 Thames port
11 Push back
12 Not in mint condition
13 Punctuation mark
17 Power
18 Sport
22 Sea mammal
23 Mesh
24 Wall painting
25 Zephyr

DOWN

1 Unpaid player
2 Small frying pan
3 Cancel
4 Ancient horsedrawn vehicle
5 Skilled
6 Sacred song
9 Musical instrument
14 License (anag.)
15 Evergreen tree
16 Mixed breed of dog
19 Fast
20 Shelter
21 Aft of vessel

ACROSS

1 Very small spot
4 Light, pleasing touches
8 Word opposite in meaning to another
9 General rule or principle
10 Cotton fabric
11 Lattice-work structure
13 Plant yielding bitter juice
15 Gorge
17 Insult
20 Festival
22 Reddish purple
24 Willow used in basketwork
26 Firm hold
27 Circus-swing
28 Colonist
29 Meaning

DOWN

1 Calumny
2 Devoured
3 Relative
4 Love-apple
5 Hiding-place for treasure
6 Fielding position in cricket (4-3)
7 Air-cavity in bone
12 Remainder
14 Departed
16 Idle rover
18 One-piece, tight garment
19 Torture
21 Christian festival
22 Sorcerer
23 Kingdom in South Asia
25 Boadicea's tribe

47

ACROSS

1 Outlets for smoke
7 Small nails
8 Practically
9 Regret
10 Close
11 Latin poet
13 Wound
14 Whole
17 Infuriate
18 Cicatrice
20 Cravat
22 Exciting experience
23 Register
24 Tawdry finery

DOWN

1 Assembly of witches
2 Incursions
3 Common sense
4 Cowardly
5 Frighten
6 Concentrated extract
7 Despotism
12 Hearty
13 Tanned skin
15 Contain
16 Colorado state capital
17 Joyful
19 Scratchy in tone
21 Bargain

ACROSS

1 Male address
4 Luck
7 Defamed
9 Hard wood
10 Vale
11 Cutting weapon
13 Dried grape
14 French existentialist
15 Large chest
17 Madhouse
19 Paddled deeply
20 Succulent root-plant
22 Eastern continent
23 Hazardous
24 Rubber
25 Swindled

DOWN

1 Teacher
2 Converse
3 Fame
4 Drinking cry
5 Retired for the night
6 Feeble
7 Content
8 Immortal
11 Fibrous tissue
12 Challenged
15 Repair shoes
16 Forest keeper
17 Stretcher carrier
18 Surrounded by water
21 Russian news agency
22 Motor car

49

ACROSS
1 Gorse
4 Held back
9 Make hot
10 Cherish
11 Unwilling
12 Storm about
13 Crib translation
14 Might
16 Designation
18 Make incision
20 Bell tongue
21 Box
24 Musical drama
25 Animal science
26 Hit
27 Governor

DOWN
1 Weakness
2 Put in new repair
3 Jacob's brother
5 Type of apartment block
6 Mary a Dr.! (anag.) (4-3)
7 Oil-fuelled engine
8 Noisily gay
13 Back pack
15 Unpaid sportsman
17 Exclusive news items
18 Fad
19 Petition
22 Rove for plunder
23 Pleasure trip

ACROSS
1 Ruled
5 Apportion
8 Territory of North-West Canada
9 Miser
10 Volatile
12 Female bird
13 Awning
14 Irritates
17 Fuss
18 Counterpane
20 Fancy
21 Outcome
23 Encounters
24 Highbrow

DOWN
1 Verse
2 Writing fluid
3 Uninterrupted (3-4)
4 European river
5 Corner
6 Abhorrent
7 News
11 Continuous gunfire
13 Skull
15 Pinching
16 Stick
18 Perfect happiness
19 Awe
22 Observe

51

ACROSS

1 Solitary
4 Small bottle
8 Morsel of bread
9 Forsake
10 Liquorice flavour
11 Way out
12 Affirmative
14 Close
15 Detect
18 Singular
21 Pain
23 Clothing
25 Seasonal wind
26 Heath genus
27 Silk-like fabric
28 Be present

DOWN

1 Informal party
2 Sustain
3 Words of an opera
4 Fruit
5 Table of contents
6 Extent
7 Confectionery
13 Ten dimes (anag.)
16 Exact
17 Hit hard
19 Lazy bee
20 Seashore
22 Royal name
24 Gift

ACROSS
1 Fairness
5 Fireplace
8 Abnormal production of nature
9 Designed
10 Science of heavenly bodies
12 Single
13 Shake with cold
14 Bone in forearm
17 Assistance
18 Very sweet substance
20 Spectre
21 Go into
23 Large area of sea
24 Repeat

DOWN
1 Large variety of orange
2 Prosecute at law
3 Vexatious
4 Use, provide work for
5 European country
6 Venetian boatman
7 Incessant
11 Inferior (5-4)
13 Wash scalp and hair
15 Attain by hard work
16 Edible large prawns
18 Lustrous silk material
19 Tend the sick
22 Afternoon meal

53

ACROSS
1 Slice of meat
4 Wealth
10 Contrition
11 Bury
12 Tale
13 Source of petroleum (3-4)
15 Consumes
17 Disreputable
19 Wrathful
22 Otherwise
25 Wordy
27 Furiously angry
29 Indian washerman
30 Trenchant
31 Goblin
32 Drone

DOWN
2 Argentine dance
3 Vexed
5 Windowed recess
6 Implore
7 Convulsive movement
8 Spartan slave
9 Amusing
14 Egyptian goddess
16 Affirmative votes
18 Whale spear
20 Akin
21 Dodge
23 Bloodsucker
24 Proverb
26 Hatred
28 Thin dress material

ACROSS

1 Urban lane
4 Hair-dresser
9 No longer at work
10 Cassia pods
11 Hard biscuit
12 Share in
13 Confirmed drunkard
14 Encounter
16 Ship's company
18 Nine-tailed whip
20 Generous
21 Trunk of plant
24 Xmas hymn
25 Canadian policeman
26 Carelessly made
27 Subject

DOWN

1 Polar glow
2 Water-lily
3 Heavy thread
5 Not concrete
6 Dressing for wound
7 Peruser
8 Experienced
13 Frightened
15 Ban
17 Groups of sheep
18 Scale
19 Measure of current
22 Church tax
23 Leave

55

ACROSS

1 Unrevealed
4 Small medicine bottle
8 Indian coin
9 Cavalry soldier
10 Rebounded
11 Hint
12 Yelp
14 Hardy heroine
15 Wild revel
18 River in Scotland
21 Instrument of torture
23 Goods transport
25 Golf club
26 Get up
27 Tasmanian wolf
28 Search out persistently

DOWN

1 Penman
2 Gelatine case for dose
3 School task
4 Study laboriously
5 Instigate
6 Pantry
7 Musical exercise
13 The common people
16 Moving ice-mass
17 Of France
19 Military cloth
20 Modest
22 Ship's anchor rope
24 Passport endorsement

56

ACROSS

1 Orange-pink substance secreted by marine polyps
4 Fellowship
8 Large crustacean
9 Edge
10 Beneath
11 Hold spellbound
13 Counter-tenor
15 Simply
17 Boil gently
20 Bobbin
22 Toffee
24 Lamp
26 Excuse
27 First
28 Clergyman's revenue
29 Situated

DOWN

1 Refinement
2 Raging
3 Printer's error
4 Water-ice
5 Venetian navigator
6 Concise witticism
7 Country bumpkin
12 Nozzle
14 Old stringed instrument
16 Young pilchard
18 Ailment
19 Withdrew
21 Ran away to wed
22 Embrace
23 Indian corn
25 Culpability

57

ACROSS

7 Mark of esteem
8 Holiday afloat
10 Refuse
11 Son of Abraham
12 Neat
13 Underworld river
17 Correspond
18 Talon
22 Raise with tackle
23 Deeply emotional
24 Obvious
25 Stick

DOWN

1 Needing a drink
2 No-one in particular
3 Roman god of love
4 Cargo
5 Italian city
6 Soft fruit
9 Hit in cafe (anag.)
14 Feign
15 Fabric
16 Add sugar
19 Form
20 Same again
21 Pore over

ACROSS

1 U.S. roadside restaurant
4 Power
10 Tourist
11 Throw
12 Viper
13 Fruit
15 Money-drawer
17 Famous racecourse
19 Oneness
22 Besides
25 2nd century Greek astronomer
27 Arm-joint
29 Compact, concise
30 Disbeliever
31 English diarist
32 Swift

DOWN

2 Homer's epic poem
3 Strong grass
5 Deduce
6 Tonsorial crop
7 Book of maps
8 Nuisance
9 Gemstone
14 Sign of addition
16 Newspaper piece
18 Whip
20 Necessary
21 Lasting ill-will
23 Songlike poem
24 Bulge out
26 Foe
28 Move, stir

59

ACROSS
1 Slowing down
5 Indicate
8 Tsarist decree
9 Fowling-piece
10 Suitable
12 Nothing
13 Turn informer
14 Last Saxon king
17 Snare
18 Mad
20 Repeat
21 Make speech
23 Surrey racecourse
24 Visionary

DOWN
1 Publisher's puff
2 Literary 4
3 Sloth
4 Tittle-tattle
5 Tine of fork
6 Artless
7 Confused
11 Perfect
13 Dawn
15 Windflower
16 Climb
18 Sacred song
19 Gloomy
22 Branch

ACROSS
1 Expectorating
7 Religious sculpture
8 Checker
9 Great noise
10 Lower side of body
11 Ample
13 Summary
14 Milk/flour mixture
17 Reaping hook
18 Distinguished aviators
20 Plunge
22 Nuclear hazard
23 In cipher
24 Freed

DOWN
1 Motionless
2 Breathe in
3 Long journey
4 Stinging weed
5 HMS Victory's captain
6 Wander
7 Persian
12 Throw away
13 Forecast
15 Battle plans
16 Greasy mud
17 Digging tool
19 Church conference
21 Track of ship

61

ACROSS
- **1** Grazing
- **5** Tests
- **8** Coarse
- **9** Repetition from memory
- **10** 18th century cartoonist
- **11** Projecting stage
- **12** Butcher's pin
- **14** Horse box
- **17** Shaving implement
- **19** Ancient vehicle
- **22** Blood-sucker
- **23** Bread maker
- **24** Telling fibs
- **25** Braced framework

DOWN
- **1** Scorch
- **2** Nestle
- **3** Doorkeeper
- **4** Of the soil
- **5** Charm
- **6** Thespian
- **7** Not a sound!
- **12** Contract and wrinkle
- **13** Personal ornament
- **15** Joint of beef
- **16** Receive
- **18** Animated corpse
- **20** Move at easy pace
- **21** Concise

ACROSS
7 British artist
8 German composer
10 Deferential esteem
11 Deputy doctor
12 Bathing-beach
13 Instruct
17 Retinue
18 Brooklet
22 Lid
23 Burdensome
24 Style
25 Splendour

DOWN
1 Frighten
2 Holy war
3 Gem
4 Wizard
5 Decree
6 Scale
9 Heed
14 Mercy
15 Quick retort
16 Consecrated
19 Rascal
20 Quits
21 Hesitate

63

ACROSS
1 Scorching
7 Ill-tempered
8 A sprinter (anag.)
9 Old measurement of length
10 Inheritor
11 Improving
13 English diarist
14 Laud
17 Gambler
18 Pain
20 Hawthorn
22 Debated
23 Slack
24 Moored

DOWN
1 Capture
2 Greed
3 Coarse file
4 Sounds
5 Card game
6 Set apart
7 One hundred
12 Deadly poison
13 Illustration
15 Front tooth
16 Period of instruction
17 Power-cable support
19 Terminated
21 Hurry

ACROSS

1 Author of "The Hunting of the Snark"
5 Passenger ship
8 Air cavity in skull
9 Figure
10 Repugnant
12 Climbing plant
13 Cattle food
14 Having slipped
17 Priest's vestment
18 Conjurer's exclamation (3,6)
20 Wheel clumsily
21 Sheep's cry
23 Long, narrow crest
24 Bullfighter

DOWN

1 Conspirator in "Julius Caesar"
2 Single in cricket
3 Regard attentively
4 Tarry
5 Boundary
6 Flower
7 Rebroadcast
11 Stubborn, bigoted
13 Overpraise
15 Tumbler
16 Athenian school
18 Fence of bushes
19 Aquatic animal
22 Object aimed at

65

ACROSS
1 Expressed audible yearning
4 Russian plain
7 Estimating
9 Finishes
10 Gaelic tongue
11 Foreign
13 Way out
14 Fell in showers
15 Oriental sailor
17 In contention (2,4)
19 Close and damp
20 Notion
22 Poker stake
23 Industry
24 Elevates
25 Free from silt

DOWN
1 Plan
2 Sibilant sound
3 Abides
4 Nun
5 Sea-eagle
6 Surpass
7 Spoken to
8 Thin silk fabric
11 Tea-growing Indian state
12 Spruce
15 Linger
16 Red jewels
17 Concurred
18 Boil
21 Intentions
22 Land measure

ACROSS

7 In elevated way
8 Levered open
10 One of independent means
11 Male duck
12 Window frame
13 Jammed
17 Facial hair
18 Indigent
22 Characteristic
23 Oriental
24 Lose weight
25 Famous bridge engineer

DOWN

1 Foster lovingly
2 Worry excessively
3 Killed in battle
4 Result of multiplication
5 Test metal
6 Common snake
9 Brotherly
14 Get a new supply
15 Satisfied
16 Flow in drops
19 Tale
20 Bow-legged
21 Jewelled headgear

67

ACROSS

1 Pen-pushers
5 Rule
8 Use a broom
9 Movement over aircraft skin
10 Indispensable
12 Fuss
13 Covered with cracks
14 Comeback
17 Beast
18 Washerwoman
20 Senseless
21 Tropical fruit
23 Symbol
24 Schoolboy's food store

DOWN

1 Desert
2 Hard water
3 Efface
4 Stationary
5 Of the country
6 Peevishness (3,6)
7 No women (anag.) (3,4)
11 Knockabout comedy
13 Ceremonial carriage
15 Prevalent in area
16 Melodious
18 Ancient language
19 An American Indian
22 Gist

ACROSS

1 One-horse carriage
7 Adhere
8 Concentrated
9 Energy
10 Fate
11 Loquacious
13 Opening
14 Miracle
17 Consecrate
18 Record
20 Cretan mount
22 Potassium nitrate
23 Distressed
24 Postponed

DOWN

1 Window covering
2 Result
3 Departed
4 Dismount
5 Giddy
6 Captain
7 Part
12 Eye specialist
13 Card game
15 Fishing boat
16 Sheepdog
17 Rigorous
19 Belief
21 Fencing sword

69

ACROSS

1 Travelling shows
4 Gratify
9 Facsimile
10 Stop
11 Fine fabric
12 Guard
13 Secret agent
14 Prepare for publication
16 Foal's father
18 Prompt
20 Weird
21 At liberty
24 Greek letter
25 Salad vegetable
26 Dwell
27 Pattern of excellence

DOWN

1 Woodland area
2 Force
3 Cream off
5 Team game
6 Unpaid performer
7 Chooses
8 Content
13 Flag
15 Victorian novelist
17 Wit
18 Two-wheeled transport
19 Show
22 Circular
23 Article

ACROSS
1 Permitted
5 Poet, author of "The Highwayman"
8 Sharpened on whetstone
9 Crossbred hunting dog
10 Able to pay debts
11 Wear away
12 Threat
14 Snake
17 Sea-foam
19 Coolness of manner
22 Increase loudness
23 Bring upon oneself
24 Furze
25 Sirius (3,4)

DOWN
1 One of "The Three Musketeers"
2 Wool fat
3 Golf club
4 Add water
5 Children's room
6 Brutish person
7 Ship's doctor
12 Wild horse
13 Narrow fissure
15 French bean
16 Worn into loose threads
18 Top part of shoe
20 Oscillate
21 Mistake

71

ACROSS
1 Pastime
4 Husky
9 Roman goddess of wisdom
10 Uses a sieve
11 Always
12 Cradle song
13 Procure
14 Part in play
16 Minute
18 Chopper
20 Obvious
21 Cougar
24 Snapshot
25 Cough mixture
26 Oppose
27 Unadorned

DOWN
1 Hinder
2 Spree
3 Story
5 Out of date
6 Chorus
7 Tries
8 Underground chamber
13 Bountiful
15 Threatening
17 Custodian
18 Coral island
19 Clergyman
22 Extreme
23 Bargain

ACROSS
1 Churned cream
4 Point of time
7 Dwelt awhile
9 Dupe
10 Biblical verse
11 Intended
13 Settled debt
14 Winter stoat
15 Church dues
17 Loud nasal exhalation
19 Entitlement
20 Filthy refuse
22 Religious group
23 Stevenson novel
24 List of duties
25 Fault

DOWN
1 Menai town
2 Implement
3 Well-grounded
4 Relating to sea
5 Encounter
6 Idle gossip
7 Boisterous farce
8 Freed
11 Collier
12 English river
15 Rage
16 Wrongdoer
17 Moulded
18 Limit
21 Caledonian attire
22 Feudal servant

73

ACROSS

1 Bury
4 Tennis tournament procedure
8 One of the family
9 Suburban house
10 Giraffe-like animal
11 Theft
13 Christmastide
15 Join up
17 Struggle
20 Trotskyite (sl.)
22 Foil EEC (anag.) (3,4)
24 Triumph
26 Historic age
27 Make good
28 Fit of rage
29 Turning machine

DOWN

1 Wearying
2 Polynesian kingdom
3 What's left
4 Unmarried
5 Young eel
6 Sick spell
7 Meat juices
12 Highest male voice
14 German name
16 Become prone (3,4)
18 Useful vessel
19 Outermost
21 Famous racehorse (3,3)
22 Fatuous
23 Hungarian composer
25 German sub (1-4)

ACROSS

5 Plaintive cry
8 Trader
9 Abrogate
10 Detached
11 On the move
14 Poem
16 Snub
17 Indian port
18 Small pocket
20 Danger
24 London terminal
25 Trite
26 Instructed
27 Scatter

DOWN

1 Shatter
2 Symbolic diagram
3 Apportion
4 Conjoint
6 Good-looking
7 Maritime
12 Pertinent
13 Ponder
14 Cancelled
15 Decline
19 Egyptian god
21 Soak
22 Veracity
23 Robust

75

ACROSS
7 Twofold
8 Struggled
10 A reverse
11 Porcelain
12 Send out
13 Trap
17 Motionless
18 Sagacious
22 Overweight
23 Continuous
24 Priest (anag.)
25 Cower

DOWN
1 Homeric poem
2 Shorten
3 Implore
4 Musical entertainment
5 Once more
6 Vapour
9 Miser
14 Endeavour
15 Remote
16 Ocean (4,3)
19 Small rodent
20 Long for
21 Furious

76

ACROSS

1 Divine nourishment
4 Author of "Brideshead Revisited"
10 Of the side
11 Domestic animal
12 Trunk
13 Ruined
15 Railway system
17 Dance
19 Make reparation
22 Yawn
25 Breed of 11
27 Damp
29 Pattern of excellence
30 Island republic in N. Atlantic
31 Eerie
32 Young ox

DOWN

2 Modify
3 English county
5 Division of a church
6 Small pickling cucumber
7 Greek philosopher
8 Buffoon
9 Digging implement
14 Cut down grain
16 Character in "Othello"
18 Late in arriving
20 Violent windstorm
21 Rascal
23 Room within roof
24 Meditate, reflect
26 Loafer
28 Empty, senseless

77

ACROSS	DOWN
7 Spirit	**1** Suffocate
8 Operative	**2** Allure
10 Rushing stream	**3** Navy
11 Reception room	**4** Wife or husband
12 Every	**5** Art
13 Easily angered	**6** Trademark
17 Scope	**9** Rigorous
18 Cipher	**14** Wed
22 Hinder	**15** Condemned
23 Figure	**16** Forsaken
24 Meddle	**19** Girl's name
25 Superficial refinement	**20** Impress
	21 Warning light

ACROSS

1 Repaired shoe
4 Electrical fault
10 Resident physician
11 Refer back
12 A lament
13 Mean
15 Painful
17 Italian dish
19 Chairman's mallet
22 Snare
25 Backslide
27 Power-cable tower
29 Non-Christian
30 Sugar browning
31 Decree
32 Vulgar speech

DOWN

2 Aquatic carnivore
3 Sincere
5 Rider's mount
6 Search thoroughly
7 Blustery
8 Operatic composer
9 Soak
14 Bright star
16 Horse fodder
18 Claimed
20 Clothing
21 Foolish talk
23 Attain
24 English invader
26 Uncontrollable fear
28 Citrus fruit

79

ACROSS

1 Assembled
7 Yields
8 Brass instrument player
9 Christmas tree
10 Extreme dislike
11 Airless
13 Table bottle
14 Weak
17 Dexterous
18 Grows old
20 Small cask
22 Careless
23 Upright
24 Delayed

DOWN

1 An equal
2 Stroll
3 Observe
4 Thing
5 Improve the mind
6 I stared (anag.)
7 Small farmer
12 Open insult
13 Of London birth
15 Object of dislike
16 Mix
17 Concur
19 Positioned
21 Prevalent

80

ACROSS
1 Retinue
4 Visions
9 Ape
10 Assumed an attitude
11 Prison
12 Distinguished
13 Exclude
14 Lady Hamilton
16 Church recess
18 Unwell
20 Public conveyance
21 Blackthorn
24 Destined
25 Reveal
26 Beat soundly
27 Command

DOWN
1 Flexible rod
2 Cake decoration
3 Vivacity
5 Act of retaliation
6 Replies
7 Staid
8 Cut
13 West Indian island
15 Ogre
17 Sugared sweet
18 Progeny
19 Extreme fear
22 Furiously angry
23 Reverberate

81

ACROSS
1 Deceives
4 Moving fast
8 Propriety
9 Firearm
10 Countrified
11 Fit of temper
13 Employed
15 Devastating insect
17 Overseas
20 Highest point
22 Musically brisk
24 Clothe
26 Cheerless
27 Pledge
28 School bag
29 Intended

DOWN
1 Red leaf (anag.)
2 Happen
3 Excess
4 Distant
5 Warning signal
6 Dante's Hell
7 Ray
12 First man
14 Heavenly body
16 Gather
18 Sleeping place
19 Meal course
21 Force
22 Mountain range
23 Circumference
25 Miss Doolittle

82

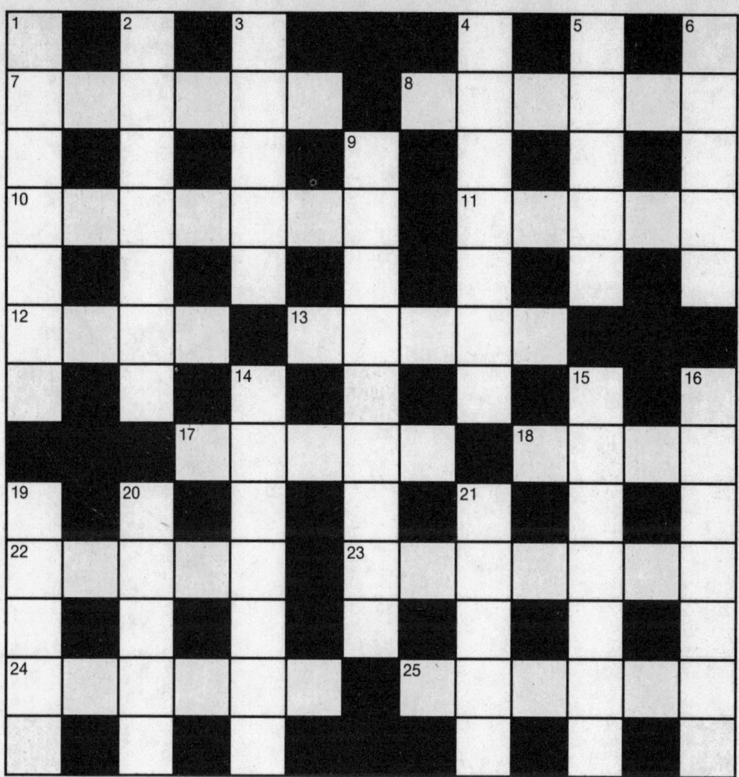

ACROSS
7 Garden City in Herts
8 Minded, watched over
10 Tutorial discourse
11 Lowest deck in ship
12 River of Central Europe
13 Open-weave fabric
17 Incorrect
18 Coffin carriage
22 Small branch, shoot
23 Fox
24 City in N. France
25 Of present times

DOWN
1 Fork-tailed bird
2 Defame
3 Thick sugary liquid
4 Waxy flower
5 Fully developed
6 Skilful, expert
9 Hired soldier
14 Member of robber band
15 Mosque tower
16 Doing business
19 Film award in form of statuette
20 Plait
21 English poet

83

ACROSS

1 Narrow street
4 Cash
10 Unfavourable
11 Play
12 Furze
13 Taverns (anag.)
15 Pace
17 Shallow dish
19 Live coal
22 Extent
25 Abandon
27 Taut
29 Occurrence
30 Deprive of courage
31 Fabulous watersnake
32 Cut

DOWN

2 Paramour
3 Sincere
5 Command
6 Issue
7 Canal boat
8 Thick
9 Rash
14 Duelling sword
16 Hard wood
18 Theft
20 Afternoon performance
21 Bid
23 Refute
24 Guide
26 Modify
28 Ravine

ACROSS
1 Rowing team
4 Beauty queens
9 Defend
10 Rub out
11 Impetuous
12 Laboratory chemical
13 Water barrier
14 Eye sore
16 Drive out
18 Atmosphere
20 Unblemished
21 Fine network
24 Madman
25 Unlawful
26 Avaricious
27 Abrasive powder

DOWN
1 Vast realm
2 Sheen
3 Long journey on foot
5 Lift
6 Idlers
7 Bed linen
8 Tempest
13 Conquered
15 White ant
17 Season
18 Top room
19 Cold
22 Bird of prey
23 Lively mirth

85

ACROSS
1 Feebly
4 Documents
7 Pillaged
9 Bemoan
10 Saucy
11 Tough cotton cloth
13 Plotted a course
14 Irish county
15 Pungent bulb
17 Eastern greeting
19 Doctrinal view
20 Fitting
22 Harbour bar
23 One who sets free
24 Small tower
25 Vigour

DOWN
1 Indian dwelling
2 Slay
3 Tugged sharply
4 Lapwing
5 Homework
6 Mowing blade
7 Small wild flower
8 A rotten do (anag.)
11 Something due
12 Words of astonishment (2,3)
15 Tricky opening move
16 Mortar
17 Governing body
18 Recollection
21 Rank
22 Skeleton substance

ACROSS
1 Hebrew judge and prophet
4 Sly looks
8 Pungent
9 Listlessness
10 Copse
11 Insect
12 Total
14 Otherwise
15 Greedy
18 Regret
21 Boast
23 Prison warder
25 Accomplish
26 Fragrance
27 Unpleasant
28 Seemly

DOWN
1 Scanty
2 Warlike
3 Imperil
4 Gasp
5 Peer
6 Expand
7 Excoriates
13 Wedlock
16 Annoying
17 Procure
19 Anaesthetic
20 Despot
22 Greenfly
24 Gainsay

87

ACROSS

1 Proffer
4 Card suit
7 Steadfastness
9 Expression of amusement (2,2)
10 Vocal composition
11 Snow and rain
13 Turn
14 Tiresome noise
15 Observing
17 Sheep
19 Drunkard
20 Smell strongly
22 Small nail
23 Spoil appearance
24 Giggle
25 Main meal

DOWN

1 Tie up
2 Facts
3 Waste materials
4 Rope for animal
5 Legislative measures
6 Insultingly ignore
7 Broken to pieces
8 County
11 Keep in short supply
12 Thin candle
15 Severe
16 Links player
17 Jammed
18 Steering vane
21 Scottish skirt
22 Grain husks

ACROSS

1 Spiteful
4 Osculated
9 Guillotine-cart
10 Internal organ
11 Harp-like instrument
12 Small species of falcon
13 Draw
14 Network
16 Leer
18 Play on words
20 Cambridge college
21 Greek war hero
24 Medicine bottle
25 Top condition
26 Gloomy
27 Old English coin

DOWN

1 Beasts of pasture
2 English river
3 Measurement
5 Apparition
6 Sundry
7 Sinisterly
8 Accidental success
13 Sensational story
15 Building
17 Foolish
18 Power-cable support
19 Not liable
22 Elephant
23 Male deer

89

ACROSS

1 Small seal on finger-ring
4 Make musical
7 Prohibited
9 Mountain lake
10 Loose scrimmage
11 Seashore
13 Secure money by intimidation
14 Oversensitive
15 Counterfeiter
17 Turning point
19 Swift
20 Crustacean
22 Material for a fire
23 Absurd
24 City of Texas
25 Mowing instrument

DOWN

1 Comfort, appease
2 Gaseous element in air
3 Small slab
4 Kidnap
5 Pour
6 Give work to
7 Brotherly
8 Flower
11 Tobacco pipe
12 Hidden stock
15 Fruitful, fertile
16 Hydrophobia
17 e.g. Lemon
18 Greet
21 Papal edict
22 Rage

ACROSS
1 Lines
3 Tinted
9 Small spot
10 Amuses
11 Stitch
13 Breed
14 Small flag
16 Cut loose
18 Military or naval action
20 Trap
22 View
23 Lament
25 Contrive
26 Remain

DOWN
1 Grates
2 Misery
4 Choice
5 Fruit-growing area
6 Setting free
7 Lineage
8 Omit
12 Nomadic
14 Suggest
15 Speech
17 Churchill's nickname
19 Knot
21 Necessitous
24 Nonsense

91

ACROSS
- **5** Living
- **8** Hardened like steel
- **9** Frighten
- **10** Hook or clip
- **11** Channel port
- **14** Grassland
- **16** Sun's halo
- **17** Heavy spanner
- **18** Expire
- **20** Declare
- **24** Runner
- **25** Squire's residence
- **26** Army officer
- **27** Bad odour

DOWN
- **1** Rigid
- **2** Accumulate
- **3** Horizontal
- **4** Respect highly
- **6** Raw
- **7** Money
- **12** Legal undertaking
- **13** Cowardly fellow
- **14** Boy
- **15** Reverential wonder
- **19** Hinder
- **21** Resentment
- **22** Book of maps
- **23** Commonplace

92

ACROSS

1 Everyman's title
4 Aim a telescope
8 Leeway
9 Forbear
10 e.g. Snake
11 Cosy
12 Juvenile goat
14 Unrestrained
15 Way out
18 Immerse
21 Kind of sandpiper
23 Brutal person
25 Of great size
26 Something added
27 Appointment to meet
28 The soul

DOWN

1 Up-to-date
2 Captain
3 Dateline (anag.)
4 Slight quarrel
5 Once more
6 Legal infancy
7 Small inlet
13 Lack of hearing
16 Foolish
17 Instigate
19 Groom the feathers
20 Breathe in
22 Suspicious
24 Elevator

93

ACROSS
1 North European language
5 Foremost
8 Taut
9 Tumbler
10 Swollen
11 Entomb
12 Stronghold
14 Rely
17 Burdened
19 Cry out
22 Obvious
23 Industrial equipment
24 Handle
25 Famous

DOWN
1 Destined
2 Baffle
3 Unskilful
4 Stores up
5 Stealthy
6 Automaton
7 Coached
12 Assemble
13 Tolerant
15 Issue
16 Mild
18 Sales campaign
20 Italian island
21 Anthem

ACROSS

1 Chess pieces
5 Seize by force
8 Vast sea
9 Berkshire town
10 Learning
12 Self
13 Abhor
14 Give in
17 Trail behind
18 Owner
20 Ordinary
21 To attempt
23 Assign
24 Quiver

DOWN

1 Rap
2 Wrath
3 Grips
4 Long step
5 Aquatic mammal
6 Outer layer of skin
7 Towing vessel
11 A long coat (anag.)
13 Quandary
15 Stringed instrument
16 Agreement
18 Braided hair
19 Verse
22 Cry

95

ACROSS

5 Woo
8 Chipping flint, etc
9 Make merry
10 Chelonian reptile
11 Piebald horse
14 Poem
16 Cricket-bat
17 Messenger
18 Fall behind
20 Entice
24 Monster of Cretan labyrinth
25 Sailing vessel
26 Melting pot
27 Black playing card

DOWN

1 Kind of ray
2 Ward off
3 Protective garment
4 Not accustomed
6 Submissive to superior
7 Discoverer of X-rays
12 Combustible gas in coal mines
13 Slovenly
14 Nocturnal bird
15 Unit of work
19 Place where bees are kept
21 Flashlight
22 Jewish religious leader
23 Sign of Zodiac

ACROSS
7 Seemly
8 Looked for
10 Strong paper
11 Not those!
12 Christmas
13 Canine skin disease
17 Cathedral town
18 Japanese liquor
22 Greek author
23 Told
24 Machine-gun from air
25 Up to date

DOWN
1 Inflexible
2 Looked over
3 Sharp bend
4 Funeral procession
5 Leered
6 Horse
9 Spanish gentleman
14 Turn to stone
15 Companion
16 Going ahead
19 Pursue
20 Clever
21 Deluge

97

ACROSS

7 Aviation pioneer
8 With anchor raised
10 Lack of rain
11 A genetic deviation
12 Fortune
13 Vagrant
17 Scandinavian imp
18 Tiny arachnid
22 Pursue
23 Captain of vessel
24 Mild earthquake
25 Maggot bait

DOWN

1 Twirl between fingers
2 Balearic isle
3 Liberals
4 Pair
5 Non-adult
6 Snapshot
9 Decontaminate
14 Liberty
15 Argument
16 Breed of dog
19 Novelist
20 Father
21 Exhausted

ACROSS

1 Apex of arch
7 Small wood
8 Poet right (anag.)
9 Large deer
10 Time or occasion
11 Middle
13 Turning like wheel
14 Lowly
17 Tree
18 Traverse swiftly
20 Hidden microphone
22 Two-hull boat
23 Irritable
24 Veteran (3-5)

DOWN

1 Two-masted vessel
2 Fermented milk food
3 Art gallery
4 Snared by loop
5 Drinking bout
6 Maritime vegetable (3,4)
7 Fabulous horse-man
12 Dodging school
13 Stage muttering
15 Coarse, stiff fabric
16 Hand-gun
17 Lustrous mineral
19 Restaurant car
21 Soot

99

ACROSS
- **1** Roosts
- **5** Small nails
- **8** Senior
- **9** Employ
- **10** Slightly wounded
- **12** Deed
- **13** Striking effect
- **14** Seem
- **17** Fasten
- **18** Elated
- **20** Fabulous animal
- **21** New Zealand aboriginal
- **23** Anaesthetic
- **24** Coming into being

DOWN
- **1** Devout
- **2** Crimson
- **3** Holder of unorthodox opinion
- **4** Looked for
- **5** Attempted
- **6** Trickery
- **7** Refuge
- **11** Fill again
- **13** Gatecrash
- **15** Nightwear
- **16** Long narrow flag
- **18** Smell
- **19** Wander aimlessly
- **22** Crude metal

ACROSS

1 Fast pace of a horse
4 Rods
8 Practice
9 Model of perfection
10 Nipped
11 Volcanic mountain
12 Pixie
14 Operatic solo
15 Shivering fit
18 Flatfish
21 Home for bees
23 Compensate
25 Set free
26 Courage
27 Vacant
28 Bludgeoned

DOWN

1 Ill-tempered
2 Beginner
3 Above
4 Wine
5 Illumination
6 Open footwear
7 Gardening implement
13 Spanish dance
16 Dig up
17 Celestial spirit
19 Short
20 Rise
22 Dwelling
24 Channel Island

101

ACROSS

1 Reinstate, make good
5 Female relatives
8 Abrupt in sound or manner
9 Repartee
10 Unnaturally sleepy
12 Deed
13 Burlesque
14 Puma
17 Grass
18 Incubus
20 Distress
21 Passage in church
23 Gentle poke or push
24 Take away, defame

DOWN

1 Brightest star in Orion
2 Former French coin
3 Ungraciously curt
4 Make angry
5 Savoury jelly
6 Homesickness
7 Protection
11 Triple
13 Person scrupulous in religion or morals
15 Pariah
16 Decided jointly
18 Illustrious
19 Cast out
22 Mineral spring

ACROSS

1 Having ringlets
4 Pigtails
9 Cuddle
10 Filament
11 Rapacious bird
12 Atrocious deed
13 Sunburn
14 Rescue
16 Swirl
18 Strange
20 Fast train
21 Roman tyrant
24 Stage play
25 Maintains
26 Ruins
27 Incantation

DOWN

1 Saucy
2 Mechanical man
3 12 months
5 Was not suitable for task
6 Reproach
7 Meat pin
8 Citrus fruit
13 Swing turn on skis
15 Pacify
17 Lea
18 Hollywood award
19 Small piece of food
22 Weird
23 Egyptian goddess

103

ACROSS
1 Conjury
4 Light case
8 American hut
9 Unspoken
10 Unskilled
11 Like candle fat
13 Divisible by two
15 Diagram in book
17 Roof makers
20 Detail in list
22 Non-Jew
24 Imitation gem
26 Arrogance
27 Storm noise
28 Given
29 Ate formally

DOWN
1 Huge dog
2 Domestic birds
3 Idle talk
4 Papal representative
5 South African province
6 Surround
7 Spruce
12 Poker stake
14 Face-net
16 Blue alpine plant
18 Confiscate
19 Killed by shaft
21 Tried out
22 Opened mouth wide
23 Chemically inactive
25 African republic

104

ACROSS
- **1** Town on Tweed
- **5** Political body
- **8** Verticality
- **9** Experiences again
- **10** Irritated
- **11** Mohammedan world
- **12** Eastern head covering
- **14** Irregular stripe
- **17** Hang down
- **19** Courage
- **22** Grudging spender
- **23** Consecrate
- **24** Church council
- **25** Churchill

DOWN
- **1** Set of exam questions
- **2** World's middle belt
- **3** Written defamation
- **4** Long step
- **5** Reader of hands
- **6** Vie
- **7** Moslem woman's veil
- **12** News
- **13** Extol
- **15** Obvious
- **16** Unreal thing
- **18** Piped musical instrument
- **20** Redbreast
- **21** Builder in stone

105

ACROSS
1 Seize forcibly
4 Self-confident
8 Discloses
9 Capital of Jordan
10 Outcome
11 Expand
13 Nought
15 Give up
17 Norwegian explorer
20 Automatic gun
22 Rodent with cheek pouches
24 Welcome
26 Face-guard of helmet
27 Wordy discussion
28 Ludicrous
29 Rustic

DOWN
1 Fighting man
2 Sprites
3 Swinging crossbar
4 Reply
5 Little
6 Comments
7 Blockhead
12 Not any
14 Irish Gaelic
16 Retribution
18 Bony
19 Unaffected
21 Treble
22 Remain in suspense
23 Pulsate
25 Young eel

106

ACROSS

1 e.g. Cockney
7 Gown
8 Lowest female voice
9 Anger
10 Abominable snowman
11 Afternoon nap
13 Flexible
14 Highly-seasoned sausage
17 Instant
18 — Lynn, singer
20 Expected
22 Talkative
23 Backbone
24 Impassioned

DOWN

1 Fortunate
2 Continuous
3 Monster
4 Choux pastry confection
5 Sources of information
6 African spear
7 Sirius (3,4)
12 Covering of feathers
13 Wood particles
15 One name (anag.)
16 False
17 Worthiness
19 Advantage
21 Obstinate animal

107

ACROSS

1 Region of S.W. Central Asia
5 Native of Moravia
8 Gemstone
9 Defamatory statement
10 Shoulderbag of canvas
12 Grain
13 Enclosure for cattle on ranch
14 e.g. Lodestone
17 Staining substance
18 Rapidity
20 Drape
21 Din
23 Province of E. Belgium
24 Rudiment

DOWN

1 Two-masted vessel
2 Vital juice
3 Polish dance
4 Rogue
5 Chink
6 Lasting quality
7 Crops gathered in
11 Bones of spine
13 Supplement to a will
15 Sideways
16 One betrothed
18 Vibrate
19 Odour
22 Rage

108

ACROSS

1 Grieving
7 Splendour
8 Hosiery town
9 Prescribed
10 Castle
11 Brief look
13 Stupefy
14 Daintily attractive
17 Smear
18 Neat
20 Statute
22 Good breeding
23 Nanny
24 Roller-shaped object

DOWN

1 Back tooth
2 Unvarying
3 Christmas
4 Stinging plant
5 Use divining rod
6 Enigma
7 Barn
12 Allay
13 Roman goddess of war
15 Lingered
16 Employment bureau
17 Brand
19 Civic dignitary
21 Puccini heroine

109

ACROSS
1 Knocked gently
4 Reply
7 Pirate
9 Aspersion
10 Pool
11 Musical instrument
13 Wring out
14 Of photographs, having poor definition
15 Tropical bird
17 Strait of English Channel
19 Bowler's approach (3,2)
20 e.g. Consommé
22 Skin disease
23 Extraction
24 Calculate
25 Seniors

DOWN
1 Soft, absorbent paper
2 Rain heavily
3 Fraud
4 Sun shelter
5 Check, dam
6 Cure
7 Crowfoot
8 Dwelling place
11 Previous
12 Lowest deck in ship
15 Shepherd
16 Soup dish
17 Fine, ingenious
18 City of ancient Egypt
21 Bundle
22 Advanced in years

110

ACROSS

1 Virgins
5 Be an informer
8 Manner
9 Vacuous statement
10 Out (3,2,4)
12 Murmur softly
13 Took long steps
14 Dismantled the camp
17 Sink a snooker ball
18 New York island
20 Queen Victoria died here
21 Stone-sharpened
23 Act of stealing
24 Fishing vessel

DOWN

1 Secret fraternity member
2 Evergreen climber
3 Voted in
4 Wooer
5 Tranquillity
6 Henry V's battlefield
7 Cone of cut, drying grass
11 Rotating platform
13 Uphold
15 Windpipe
16 Taint with disease
18 Deserve
19 Drain (anag.)
22 Zero

111

ACROSS

7 Reward (anag.)
8 Card game
10 Give back
11 Abide
12 Shortly
13 Part of fork
17 Tailor's model
18 Beak
22 Freshwater fish
23 Wandering
24 Bridge for travelling crane
25 Pressing

DOWN

1 Speech
2 Large house
3 Wading bird
4 Neptune's spear
5 Farewell
6 Pares
9 Severe rebuke
14 Refinement
15 Violinist
16 Appease
19 Raised platform
20 Injury
21 Fashionable

ACROSS
1 Hooligans
4 Resistant
8 Fowl
9 Carry out
10 Meticulous
11 Eyesore
12 Canine
14 Girl's name
15 Finished
18 Church seat
21 Curved span
23 Encourage
25 Vigorous
26 Cereal
27 Old coin
28 Clergyman

DOWN
1 Formula
2 Indefinite number
3 Encumbrance
4 Conservative
5 Submarine (1-4)
6 Picnic basket
7 Go fast
13 Web-like material
16 Building
17 Frank
19 Hoisting machine
20 Choose
22 Scoffer
24 Leave out

113

ACROSS

1 Town in Co. Down
4 Quest
9 Dense mass of trees
10 Appointments
11 English painter of nudes
12 Rubbish
13 Lad
14 Goad
16 Tax on goods
18 In the past
20 Permitted
21 Volcano in Sicily
24 Brief, concise
25 Body of aides
26 Prairie-wolf
27 Common people of ancient Rome

DOWN

1 Aromatic kernel
2 Card game
3 Oppressive burden
5 Fabled S. American city (2,6)
6 Draw in
7 Hurry on
8 Artificially histrionic
13 Bully
15 Woman's saddle horse
17 Sea in N. Europe
18 Bedeck
19 Gentle touch
22 Slight colouring
23 Desist

114

ACROSS

1 Was aware
3 One-horse carriage
9 Lively
10 Fridge compartment
11 Consume
13 Land/water creature
14 Cosset
16 Consents
18 Onlooker
20 Unhappy
22 Institute of higher learning
23 Rock plant
25 Close of day
26 Minus

DOWN

1 Oxford college
2 Samuel's guardian
4 Formula
5 Combining
6 Felicity
7 Seagoing troops
8 Predatory gull
12 Moderate
14 Corridor
15 Implore
17 Remained
19 Got up
21 French novelist
24 Expire

115

ACROSS
7 Middle
8 Package
10 Leftist group
11 Day in Roman calendar
12 Type of chop
13 Irritated
17 Exhibitionist act
18 Surfeit
22 Plain writing
23 Cavalryman
24 Knotty
25 Disclose

DOWN
1 Coal bucket
2 Tasteless
3 Arrogant
4 Artist
5 Landscape
6 Meat
9 Explosive
14 Disbelieved in God
15 Sailing vessel
16 Frighten
19 Exhausted
20 Merchandise
21 Assembly of witches

ACROSS
1 Heaven-sent food
4 Domicile
10 Utterly
11 Coffer
12 Desert plants
13 Capricious
15 Splendid
17 Remains
19 Stage-whisper
22 Lazy
25 Intention
27 Welsh dog
29 Tendency
30 Tumbler
31 Severe
32 Strangely

DOWN
2 Garret
3 Cancel
5 Hollywood award
6 Perfumed
7 Farm animals
8 God of marriage
9 Cane
14 Genuine
16 River at Oxford
18 Torture
20 Fastened
21 Flood
23 Exclude
24 Laughter
26 Command
28 Insurgent

117

ACROSS
- **5** Position taken up
- **8** Encircle
- **9** Lament
- **10** Transgressor
- **11** Laughter
- **14** Fuss
- **16** Fated
- **17** Safe
- **18** Deed
- **20** Condescend
- **24** Animate being
- **25** Trust
- **26** Postponed
- **27** Booth

DOWN
- **1** Berkshire racecourse
- **2** Wander aimlessly
- **3** Circular
- **4** Relax
- **6** Dusk
- **7** Futile
- **12** Likeness
- **13** Everlasting
- **14** Girl's name
- **15** Dismissed
- **19** Moorland bird
- **21** Rescued
- **22** Hasten
- **23** Prepared

ACROSS
- **1** Glossy
- **7** Imperfections
- **8** Agree
- **9** Yorkshire river
- **10** Comply
- **11** Set fire to
- **13** Floor covering
- **14** Small stone
- **17** Giggle
- **18** Smudge
- **20** Cry of a crow
- **22** Intermittent
- **23** Wide awake
- **24** Set out

DOWN
- **1** Musical instrument
- **2** e.g. Chartreuse
- **3** Vessel
- **4** Flag
- **5** Worth
- **6** Basic quality
- **7** Cats
- **12** Stinted (anag.)
- **13** Hide
- **15** Courageous canine
- **16** Mend
- **17** Rough woollen cloth
- **19** Went fast
- **21** Lady Hamilton

119

ACROSS
- **7** Encircling line of police
- **8** Trundled
- **10** Flexible
- **11** Cavalry sword
- **12** Stringed instrument
- **13** Poisonous
- **17** Garden flower
- **18** Volcanic discharge
- **22** Opera by Puccini
- **23** Not conscious of
- **24** Sensitive to cold
- **25** Plaster for coating walls

DOWN
- **1** Shoulder blade
- **2** Weakness
- **3** Uncertainty
- **4** Adoration
- **5** Playing cards suit
- **6** Viper
- **9** Savage, cruel
- **14** Hardy
- **15** Caribbean island
- **16** King Arthur's seat
- **19** Reserve supply
- **20** On the move
- **21** Social gathering

ACROSS

1 Embroidery yarn
4 Grab
8 Church anthem
9 Uniform
10 Waits on
11 Male deer
12 Total
14 Rind
15 Incite
18 Age
21 Jump
23 Treeless plain
25 Indifferent
26 Unsuitable
27 Walk
28 Invisible

DOWN

1 Fight
2 Qualify
3 Embroil
4 Wise
5 Creek
6 Infuriate
7 Herbage
13 Change
16 Refuse
17 Heavenly body
19 Make request
20 Defeated
22 Sharp
24 Grating

121

ACROSS
1 Old county division
5 Serves at table
8 Medicine
9 Toil
10 Navigational measurement
12 Hostelry
13 Fingerless glove
14 Wild
17 Road-surfacing material
18 Preparedness
20 Excited
21 Atmospheric gas
23 Literary composition
24 Cooked in oven

DOWN
1 Large inn
2 Member of female order
3 Take delivery of
4 Bypass
5 Aquatic mammal
6 Lifeless
7 Lack of sound
11 Of bad repute
13 Inflammable gas
15 American state
16 Prison guard
18 Corroded
19 Horse
22 Dismissed

122

ACROSS
- **1** Macabre
- **7** English blooms?
- **8** Dutifulness
- **9** Self
- **10** Handle roughly
- **11** Harmony
- **13** Wan
- **14** Call upon earnestly
- **17** Record cover
- **18** Bogus
- **20** Fruit
- **22** 19th cent. Italian patriot
- **23** Hold forth
- **24** Footwear fastener

DOWN
- **1** Tend a horse
- **2** Not uniform
- **3** Spadeful
- **4** Threat
- **5** Requested
- **6** Take in marriage
- **7** Spring back
- **12** Part in different directions
- **13** Spectre
- **15** She loved Hamlet
- **16** Act to excess
- **17** Leather thong
- **19** Corncobs
- **21** Lean against

123

ACROSS

1 24 sheets of paper
4 Anchored floats
10 Takes away
11 Progeny
12 Napery
13 Diet
15 Spanish artist
17 Urge forward
19 Unsteady
22 Girl's name
25 Herring-like fish
27 Dig
29 Porcelain
30 Accounts
31 Concur
32 Trembling poplar

DOWN

2 Emasculate
3 Retaliation
5 Employing
6 Moslem veil
7 Ruffle
8 Shylock's trade
9 Sham attack
14 Merit
16 King of Norway
18 Assembly
20 Antigone's father
21 Cavalry weapon
23 Approaches
24 Animal
26 Reflection
28 Big

ACROSS
1 Pastime
4 Husky
9 Ore
10 Uncommon
11 Effortless
12 Cloud formation
13 Tint
14 Associate
16 Requirement
18 Heavy drinker
20 Skull
21 French priest
24 Greek letter
25 Countermand
26 Hide from sight
27 Simple-minded villager

DOWN
1 East coast estuary
2 Extra payment
3 Measure
5 Decorative piece
6 Gyrate
7 Join up
8 Carroll heroine
13 Fragile
15 Unpaid performer
17 Thespians
18 Chic
19 Genetics scientist
22 Bat an eyelid
23 Catch sight of

125

ACROSS

7 Cricket dismissal (3,3)
8 High regard
10 Scarf
11 Open sore
12 Cheerful song
13 Green turf
17 Proboscis
18 Bloodsucking insect
22 Freshwater fish
23 Garden vegetable
24 Find fault in petty manner
25 Stately, sombre

DOWN

1 Blackberry bush
2 Capture, purloin
3 Oppressor of the weak
4 Charnel house
5 Common forest tree
6 Smile smugly
9 Elevated lookout on ship (5,4)
14 e.g. Cowslip
15 Cured herring
16 Laundry
19 Hard wood
20 Horse's cry
21 Garfunkel partner

126

ACROSS

1 Permission
5 Scolded
8 Shrink from fear
9 Victory
10 Dip into water
11 Extreme
12 Prohibited
14 Custodian
17 Famous
19 Detonate
22 Futile
23 Greenfly
24 Lock of hair
25 Abridge

DOWN

1 Prickly plants
2 Reporter
3 Mistake
4 Sampled
5 Hermit
6 Midlands river
7 Hopelessness
12 Feast
13 Incessant
15 Seer
16 Against
18 Subject
20 Greek philosopher
21 Ruhr steel centre

127

ACROSS	DOWN
1 Buddhist concept of merit	**2** Month
4 Of little weight	**3** Fictional detective
10 Cavalry weapon	**5** Angry
11 Possession	**6** Coarse sacking
12 Straight-edge	**7** Twenty
13 Vent	**8** English novelist
15 Large jug	**9** Platform
17 Box	**14** Poke
19 Express opinion	**16** Water shaft
22 Vein of ore	**18** Pillage
25 Seek advice	**20** Worry
27 Drive away	**21** Mountain gravel
29 Precise	**23** River animal
30 Outshine	**24** Group of vessels
31 Female attire	**26** Speak
32 Additional	**28** Scottish musician

ACROSS

1 Roman dictator
4 Opportunity
7 Onlooker
9 Mountain goat
10 Illegal drug
11 Small inlet
13 Airstrip
14 Fraudulent activity
15 Military commission
17 Raiding excursion
19 Intoxicated
20 A heavy blow
22 Caught thread
23 Interim (4,5)
24 Anticipate
25 Lithe

DOWN

1 Sturgeon roe
2 River of Hades
3 Turning like wheel
4 Zodiac sign
5 Matured
6 Skilful
7 Jollification
8 Zooming skywards
11 Showed concern
12 Cushion stuffing
15 Talk incessantly
16 Most faithful
17 Jibes
18 Machine
21 Animal skin
22 Bargain

129

ACROSS
1 Posting
5 Hungarian composer
8 Severe
9 Authors
10 Throw a party
12 Gratuity
13 Piece of soap
14 Tap
17 Equality
18 Relevant
20 Small house
21 Cancel
23 Shelf
24 Builder

DOWN
1 Pleasant sound
2 Frozen water
3 Base
4 Bauble
5 French river
6 Sight
7 Drunkard
11 Freed
13 Characteristic
15 Living
16 Mourn
18 Spot
19 Roofing specialist
22 Snare

ACROSS
1 Pretentious
7 Beneficiaries
8 Seaside walk
9 Nocturnal bird
10 Way out
11 German town
13 Propose
14 Select
17 Withdraw
18 Hitch
20 Before
22 Unhappy
23 Sarah (dim.)
24 Killer

DOWN
1 Fruit
2 Flower seller
3 Ship's company
4 Jubilant
5 American buffalo
6 Set apart
7 Fit
12 Science of body structure
13 Back to front
15 Public transport
16 Turning point
17 Answer
19 Colour
21 Square measurement

131

ACROSS

1 Ordinary riding horses
4 Great church
8 Syrup-like medicine
9 Injury
10 Soup
11 Made of clay
13 Nobleman
15 Lags behind
17 Suit of playing cards
20 Thunder-god
22 Sign of Zodiac
24 Type of finger
26 — Marbles, famous sculptures
27 Wine shop
28 Cavity in road surface
29 Send money

DOWN

1 Fish
2 River of Africa
3 Schoolbag
4 Assemble soldiers
5 More recent
6 Slightly unsound mentally
7 French sculptor
12 As well
14 Italian wine
16 In the midst of
18 e.g. Lithographer
19 Navigational instrument
21 Walk awkwardly
22 Precipitous
23 Piebald horse
25 Distant hope

ACROSS
1 Dormant
7 Origin
8 Complicated
9 Nothing
10 Appointment
11 Modifies
13 Divine beverage
14 Corsair
17 Beast
18 Lacerate
20 Cobbler's tool
22 Estranged
23 Even
24 Bullfighter

DOWN
1 Velocity
2 Flexible
3 Conspiracy
4 Almost
5 Fetters
6 Communion-cup
7 Advantage
12 Excellent
13 Distinguished
15 Put on guard
16 Gaming-house
17 In existence
19 Horseman
21 Formerly

133

ACROSS
1 Power
4 Diners
9 Socialist
10 Recorded
11 Finished
12 Antiphon
13 Fruit seed
14 Jacob's brother
16 Act
18 Bishopric
20 Type of bean
21 Indonesian island
24 Police car
25 Cooking room
26 Slimmed
27 Mean person

DOWN
1 Chap
2 Infantry weapon
3 Way out
5 Stance
6 Blow up
7 Dignified
8 Denude
13 Buy
15 Injecting instrument
17 Formed
18 Feed with fuel
19 Method
22 Garden mite
23 Stalk

ACROSS

1 Ties
4 Permitted
8 Roman magistrate
9 Tennis score
10 Reside
11 Turned from sideways (2-5)
13 Notion
15 Mock
17 Secret envy
20 Run from danger
22 Exchange
24 Arbiter
26 Souvenir
27 Nourishment
28 Sincere
29 Soon

DOWN

1 American grasshopper
2 Suppose
3 Sordid
4 Leafy road
5 Branch of freemasons
6 Injured
7 Terror
12 e.g. Buttons
14 Clever
16 Meanderer
18 Exult
19 In upright manner
21 East Mediterranean shores
22 Imprecate
23 Pawnbroker (sl.)
25 Cheerless

135

ACROSS
1 Small
4 Stray
7 Thanks
9 Venture
10 Terminates
11 Precipitous
13 Revolve
14 Save
15 Rogue
17 Chaff
19 Captured
20 Unhappy
22 Account
23 Art of public speaking
24 Fraud
25 Take ill

DOWN
1 Pantry
2 Weed
3 Domain
4 Fade
5 Knot
6 Price of liberation
7 Bizarre
8 Amuse
11 Ermine
12 Hickory
15 Scurrilous
16 Surgical instrument
17 Improved
18 Soften
21 Otherwise
22 Forepart of ship

136

ACROSS

1 Shellfish
4 Leap
8 Take a firm hold
9 Gun
10 Deeply emotional
11 Blood vessel
12 Dispute
14 Soon
15 Rim
18 Fasten
21 Swedish pop group
23 Hand over
25 Female side
26 Frequently
27 One slow to learn
28 Farce

DOWN

1 Bird
2 Austere
3 Open next (anag.)
4 Grain store
5 Practice
6 Insist upon
7 Tender
13 Prosperous (4-2-2)
16 Old-fashioned dance
17 Came down
19 Improve the mind
20 Spirit
22 Member of ship's crew
24 Dial

137

ACROSS

1 Aid in distress
5 Set of rooms
8 In darkness
9 Stain, reproach
10 Christmas entertainment
12 Unwell
13 Destitute person
14 Port in S.E. Lincolnshire
17 Mineral spring
18 Person of undisclosed ability (4,5)
20 Sinful
21 Midday meal
23 Exhilarate
24 Soup ingredients

DOWN

1 Sudden decline
2 Mountain depression
3 Result
4 Cony
5 Undressed kid
6 Originator
7 Stepwise arrangement of troops
11 Pain along course of nerve
13 Bodily attitude
15 The Moor of Venice
16 Chalk pencil
18 Evade
19 Moral significance
22 Zero

138

ACROSS

7 Hairdresser
8 Pigtails
10 Increase
11 Illustrious
12 Not any
13 Trite
17 Rustic
18 Healthy
22 Oscillate
23 Learned
24 Yawning
25 Noiseless

DOWN

1 Procures
2 Bandit
3 Make merry
4 Former
5 Corpulent
6 Willow
9 Ruse
14 Acrid
15 Sailor
16 Under
19 Custom
20 Chillingly cold
21 Flinch

139

ACROSS

1 Brief
4 Alter
9 Dampen
10 Rare animal
11 Citrus fruit
12 Return to ill health
13 Small bed
14 Greek porch
16 Scullery tub
18 Pack animal
20 Ring-shaped
21 Hurry
24 Giver
25 Warship
26 Feel anger towards
27 Fretted

DOWN

1 Specimen
2 Hard drug
3 Gambling office
5 Despairing
6 Skittle
7 Rubber
8 Contemptuous grunt
13 Iron cooking pot
15 Lessees
17 Prison guard
18 Betel-nut palm
19 Distributed
22 Fire-raising
23 Gibe

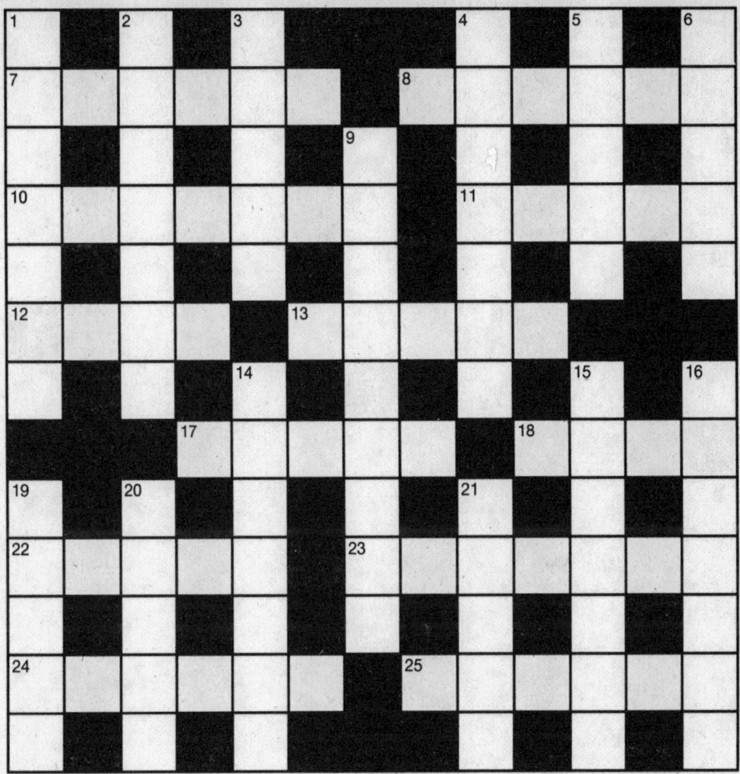

ACROSS
- **7** Diminutive
- **8** Digit
- **10** Disturb
- **11** Lustre
- **12** Reflected sound
- **13** Less important
- **17** Sea gasteropod
- **18** Swing round
- **22** Dowdy woman
- **23** Brass instrument
- **24** Shun
- **25** Set of eight

DOWN
- **1** Sparkle
- **2** Wasting away
- **3** The earth
- **4** Vocation
- **5** Monstrous creatures
- **6** Seaside promenade
- **9** Make laws
- **14** Monstrous lie
- **15** London rail junction
- **16** Bandaged
- **19** Subsequently
- **20** Puppet hunchback
- **21** Charlatan

141

ACROSS
1 Forgo
4 Farewell
8 Brave
9 Fertiliser
10 Honey-badger
11 Serious
13 Strays
15 Death
17 Sunburnt
20 Wicked
22 Waterfall
24 Tropical climber
26 Trunk
27 Riverside walk
28 Capital of Nova Scotia
29 Drab

DOWN
1 Faltered
2 Arm of sea
3 Empowers
4 Collect
5 Proprietor
6 Marsh bird
7 Upright
12 Italian wine
14 Water plant
16 Cold wind in Provence
18 Permitted
19 Fatal
21 Highest point
22 Capture
23 Distant
25 Once more

142

ACROSS
1 Lumberjack
4 Slumber
8 To fish
9 Ice-like quartz
10 Greet affectionately
11 Toilet powder
12 Bundle
14 Reject
15 Reverberate
18 Cereal
21 Depend
23 Ship
25 Large bat
26 Sarcastic humour
27 Colour slightly
28 23's fireman

DOWN
1 Straw-coloured
2 Easily read
3 Lift
4 Type of bean
5 Additional
6 Royal residency
7 Twist
13 Abandoned
16 Poison
17 Neckwear
19 County
20 Orison
22 Fruit
24 Small flute

143

ACROSS

1 Weather (anag.)
5 Of a city
8 Freshwater fish
9 City of Avon
10 Unreported road accident (3-3-3)
12 High priest
13 Thin with water
14 Honest
17 Mineral spring
18 Gad about
20 Mimic
21 Spurious
23 Harvest
24 In the direction of

DOWN

1 Surveillance
2 Self
3 No longer existing
4 Herald's coat
5 State of wedlock
6 Area in London
7 Nothingness
11 Loquacious
13 Unavoidable fate
15 Iris
16 Short watch-chain
18 Magnificent
19 Burdensome jobs
22 Pike-like fish

ACROSS

1 Freight
4 Neckband
9 Vexatious sprite
10 Ant
11 Overdue
12 Rosette worn on hat
13 Tibetan ox
14 Likewise
16 Blackthorn
18 Favourite
20 Boat race meeting
21 Notion
24 Rigid
25 Clumsy
26 Pointer on dial
27 Fold

DOWN

1 Flock of geese
2 Public
3 Auction
5 Cloudy
6 Backache
7 Somewhat
8 Light meal
13 Young
15 Brown coal
17 Prayer
18 Heathen
19 Brigand
22 Male duck
23 Beehive

145

ACROSS

7 Policeman
8 Shakespearean weaver
10 Type of piano
11 Track
12 Wander
13 Trite
17 Banter
18 A long way off
22 Love
23 Part of circle
24 Intelligent
25 Card suit

DOWN

1 Insurance statistician
2 Frugal and hardy
3 Blend
4 Male servant
5 Corn stalk
6 Sufficient
9 Firm
14 Put keen edge on
15 Turkish title
16 Register complaint
19 Consignment
20 Ardent lover
21 African country

ACROSS

1 Beats
4 Functions
8 Former 10-dollar coin
9 Put on trial
10 Oppression
11 Festival
12 Annoying experience
14 Lyric poems
15 Short measure
18 Vital juice
21 Lively frolic
23 Lighthouse chamber
25 Stay a while
26 Spiteful
27 18th cent. Prime Minister
28 Edict

DOWN

1 Garland
2 Predicted
3 Intensity
4 Metal thread
5 German river
6 Offender
7 Classic goat-man
13 Ship's compass box
16 City on Dee
17 Captivity
19 Smoothing tool
20 Protein substance
22 Army rank
24 Press against

147

ACROSS
5 Hardwood tree
8 Makes
9 Nimble
10 Building
11 Censure
14 Strange
16 Shepherd
17 Florid
18 Sack
20 Diving bird
24 Almanac
25 Devil
26 Living
27 Employing

DOWN
1 Bid
2 Doorkeeper
3 Indistinct
4 Countless
6 Aubergine
7 Disaster
12 Bald
13 Obstinate
14 Globe
15 Follow closely
19 Astonished
21 Resist authority
22 Concede
23 Command

ACROSS
1 Precious stone
4 Mastery
8 Act
9 Cereal
10 Piquancy
11 Hours of light
13 River of Hades
15 Rubbish
17 Froth
20 Very old
22 Ultimate limit
24 Consternation
26 Wrath
27 Instructor
28 Playhouse
29 Strained

DOWN
1 Roman god
2 Merchandise
3 Insoles (anag.)
4 Light entertainment
5 Not at all (coll.) (2,3)
6 Type of wine, e.g. hock
7 Nimble
12 Pivoting rod
14 Sports side
16 Tiredness
18 Uncompromising
19 Sorrow
21 Mild
22 Precise
23 White heron
25 Pallid

149

ACROSS

1 Number of Ali Baba's thieves
4 Masticated
9 Smuggle liquor
10 Wild west show
11 Stringed instrument
12 Commend
13 Amateur radio operator
14 Guinea pig
16 Voracious fish
18 Side issue
20 Wickerwork boat
21 Bazaar
24 English poet
25 Soft leather
26 Boil
27 Song

DOWN

1 Bone of leg
2 Sleeping place
3 American university
5 Sailor's dance
6 Matrimony
7 One who drives cattle
8 Town in Surrey
13 Flower
15 Shorten
17 Remnants
18 Seashore
19 Worthless
22 On high
23 Settled

150

ACROSS
1 Restaurant car
4 Power
10 Intimidated
11 Abundant
12 Supple
13 Hinder
15 Memorandum
17 Short match
19 Revile
22 Narrative
25 Great pleasure
27 Boring tool
29 Donor
30 Disturb
31 Entomb
32 Quartzite gem

DOWN
2 Creek
3 Obvious
5 Senseless
6 Unfortunate
7 White poplar
8 Modify
9 Pier
14 Genuine
16 Sworn statement
18 Animate
20 Comportment
21 Proverb
23 Book of maps
24 Fish basket
26 Furze
28 Ogre

151

ACROSS

1 Observer
5 Cogitate
8 Indispensable
9 Snake
10 Told
11 Up to the time of
12 Neck passage
14 Adjournment
17 Hours of darkness
19 Chirp
22 Great sorrow
23 Jumped
24 Dug for coal
25 Deserved

DOWN

1 Sway
2 Gossip
3 Spartan serf
4 Have abode
5 Physical ill-treatment
6 Fatuous
7 Kitchen vessels
12 Fit of temper
13 Changed
15 Draw out
16 Current
18 Street urchin
20 Lazy type
21 Assessed

ACROSS

5 American republic
8 Answer
9 Talk foolishly
10 Sea sickness (3,2,3)
11 Actors' award
14 ...and so on
16 Revolving drum
17 Take retribution
18 British island
20 Young ox
24 Hindrance
25 Wood texture
26 Crazy
27 Proverb

DOWN

1 Tiny particle
2 Devotional song
3 Budged
4 Declare
6 Pestered
7 Torpor
12 Torn and ragged
13 Instructions
14 Tree
15 Tin
19 Watch-chain
21 Pile
22 Room for action
23 Trifling

153

ACROSS
1 Aggrieved
3 Dawn
9 Keen
10 Speaker's platform
11 Faint
13 Without resources
14 Crayon
16 Test performance (3,3)
18 Get rid of
20 Perceived
22 Unhurried
23 Sprite
25 Intensified
26 Feeble

DOWN
1 Rate
2 Mat
4 Apprehend
5 More vigorous
6 Talkative
7 Storm
8 Mesh
12 Chew
14 Promised
15 Gourmet
17 Scottish magistrate
19 Rim
21 Shellfish
24 Poem

ACROSS
7 Illicit romance
8 Reduced to powder
10 Academic
11 Apple drink
12 Weathercock
13 Type of willow
17 Sphere
18 Daybreak
22 Counterfeit
23 Unimportant
24 Thought
25 Stay

DOWN
1 Colossal
2 Casual
3 Firearm
4 Go ahead
5 Surpass
6 Revere
9 Bit of rest (anag.)
14 Flower
15 Natural home
16 Suspicion
19 Hard wood
20 A gemstone
21 Skinflint

155

ACROSS

1 Plunge
3 Pressingly
9 Cloth for drying
10 First coats
11 Clique
13 Private cabin
14 Provincial dialect
16 Assault
18 River port in Kent
20 Gratuity
22 Sweltering
23 Retinue
25 Marked with little spots
26 Whirlpool

DOWN

1 Appointments
2 Solemn promise
4 Iterate
5 Distinguished
6 Musically quivering
7 Double veil of Moslem women
8 European mountain range
12 Private interview (4-1-4)
14 Flying horse
15 Climber's tool (3-4)
17 Small hound
19 Tax on goods
21 Coin
24 Assistance

156

ACROSS

1 Master of ceremonies
5 Memoranda
8 English composer
9 Acrid
10 Arrives at
11 Praise highly
12 Sheep's coat
14 Common saying
17 More secure
19 Plug
22 Enrage
23 Inexpensive
24 Nick
25 Read

DOWN

1 Distinct
2 Move to another country
3 Soil
4 Uncover
5 Convent
6 Larceny
7 Paid
12 Vogue
13 Greek port
15 Govern tyrannically
16 Dormant
18 Aspect
20 Happen
21 Swift

157

ACROSS

1 Augmented note
4 Wood working
8 Behead
9 Auctioneer's hammer
10 Angry
11 Land holdings
13 London architect
15 Rowing crews
17 *Sotto voce* remarks
20 American state
22 Iranian
24 Abdominal flatulence
26 Principality
27 Friendly
28 Auburn-haired person
29 Tempests

DOWN

1 Unproductive
2 Sports enclosure
3 Wisely cautious
4 Subjects
5 Correct
6 Asked to come
7 Heraldic red
12 Playwright
14 Continent
16 Misreported
18 Hessian
19 Victory
21 Forward
22 Strength
23 Children
25 Tag

ACROSS
1 Urging forward
5 Govern
8 Legally correct
9 Setback
10 A find
12 Lubricant
13 Shine
14 Commotion
17 Groove
18 Huge crowd
20 Airman
21 Volunteer
23 Root vegetable
24 Strive against

DOWN
1 Took the plunge
2 Unfit
3 At home
4 Gemstone
5 Muster
6 Offhand
7 Goads
11 I also tire (anag.)
13 Maybe
15 Distinctive garb
16 Minister
18 Unit of length
19 Weird
22 Charge for service

159

ACROSS
- **1** Nut
- **4** Ambled
- **8** Craze
- **9** Unpoetic
- **10** Condescended
- **11** Portent
- **12** Finish
- **14** Responsibility
- **15** Image
- **18** Sorrowful
- **21** Roguish
- **23** Agony
- **25** Akin
- **26** Out of order
- **27** Yugoslav currency
- **28** Swallow-tailed flag

DOWN
- **1** Fleet of warships
- **2** Brief notice
- **3** Proximity
- **4** Conspiracy
- **5** Amulet
- **6** Seemly
- **7** Digging tool
- **13** Ignominy
- **16** View
- **17** Holy
- **19** Beau
- **20** Selected
- **22** Punctuation mark
- **24** Commotion

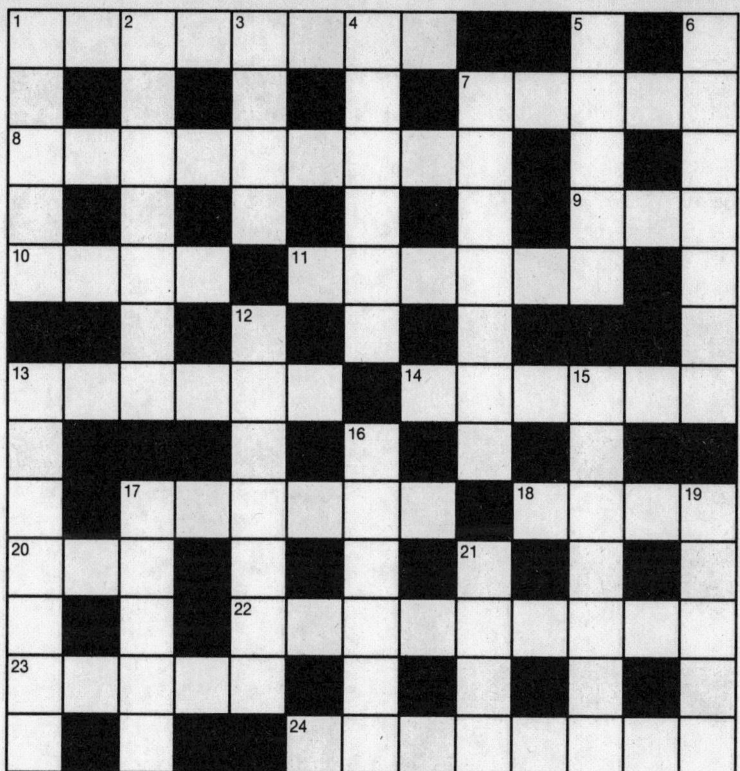

ACROSS

1 Salad oil
7 Chart
8 Throne claimant
9 The sun
10 Palm fruit
11 Pass by
13 Sponger
14 Funeral vehicle
17 Surgical stitch
18 Pack away
20 Extremity
22 Much admired
23 Edible bulb
24 Relaxed

DOWN

1 Drugged
2 Built
3 Twist
4 Small lump
5 Maltreat
6 Install substitute
7 Fur hunter
12 Reading stand
13 Heading
15 Turns
16 Very fast
17 Iberian state
19 Walked through water
21 Pile

161

ACROSS

5 Sentry
8 Gathering of women only (3,5)
9 Republic of N.E. Africa
10 Relating to navigation, shipping, etc
11 Aptitude
14 Globe
16 Solidarity leader
17 Necessitate
18 Soldier's effects
20 Furious
24 Away from land
25 Once more
26 Unripe
27 Not correct

DOWN

1 Heavy blow
2 Breathe stertorously
3 e.g. Spaghetti
4 Worthless cheque, sham (sl.)
6 Hoofed
7 Class of vertebrates including snakes
12 Feign illness
13 Agitation against authority of State
14 Tree
15 Wager
19 Ill repute
21 Easterner
22 Spurious
23 Separate, put apart

ACROSS

1 Customary
7 Old stringed instruments
8 Butter-substitute
9 Anger
10 Surprise attack
11 Away
13 Burlesque imitation
14 Court game
17 Wicket
18 Stalk
20 Total
22 Performance
23 e.g. Pancreas
24 Put in order

DOWN

1 Greek poet
2 Obstacle
3 Salver
4 Elbows out, hands on hips
5 Characteristic
6 Maintains
7 Young hare
12 Cited as evidence
13 Corridor
15 Nil
16 Seem
17 Smudge
19 Excavated
21 Cougar

163

ACROSS

1 Woman's garment
4 Within hull of ship
8 Fire-dog
9 Racket
10 Body of policemen
11 Organised travel
13 Necessity
15 Swift's flying island
17 Result of an action
20 Hindu garment
22 Mosque tower
24 Lustrous silk fabric
26 Green turf
27 Raise to peerage
28 Visitors
29 Civil wrongs

DOWN

1 Surgeon's knife
2 River of Asia
3 Afflict with great pain
4 Set fire to
5 Group of African languages
6 Coal tar product used in dyeing
7 Fantasy
12 European river
14 Relaxation
16 Kind of duck
18 Open mesh fabric
19 Bulk oil carriers
21 Hasten (anag.)
22 Art of expression in sound
23 Narrow crest
25 Underground root

164

ACROSS
1 Pungent
5 Footwear
8 Stint
9 City fortress
10 Total collapse
11 Hasten
12 Summary
14 Avoided
17 Public
19 Cut of beef
22 Wipe out
23 Governor
24 Fragrant herb
25 Foot lever

DOWN
1 Attitudinised
2 Cavil
3 Savoury jelly
4 Travel receipt
5 Scholar's bag
6 Tidiness
7 Spread out
12 Undertaking
13 Concentrated
15 Bored
16 Road with houses
18 Void
20 Purify
21 Weird

165

ACROSS
1 Fastened
5 Step
8 Set of records
9 Speedy warship
10 Raincoat
12 Pole
13 Large wood
14 Climbs
17 Prosecute
18 Make laws
20 Canadian province
21 Unlocks
23 Cool courage
24 Arctic tribesmen

DOWN
1 Frighten
2 Lie
3 Spanish grand inquisitor
4 Physician
5 Melting snow
6 Smallest continent
7 Altar-piece
11 Woodworker
13 Garland
15 Priest's garment
16 Wilfully disregard
18 Big
19 Relaxes
22 Hardwood tree

ACROSS

1 Messenger
5 Flashlight
8 Fruit
9 Positive
10 Cheese
11 Chasm
12 Common Market country
14 Beast of burden
17 Province of South Africa
19 Recipe
22 Zodiac sign
23 Card game
24 Brief fight (3-2)
25 Neither (anag.)

DOWN

1 Form
2 e.g. Crocodile
3 Bungling
4 Not long past
5 Violent wind
6 Prepared
7 Truthfulness
12 Origin
13 West Indian song
15 Finger joint
16 Exertion
18 Game fish
20 Currency unit
21 Scottish isle

167

ACROSS

1 Begin
4 Gains by work
10 Automatic piano
11 Thickset draught horse
12 Power
13 Fastening-wires
15 Twin brother of Jacob
17 Concise
19 Talk vaingloriously
22 Gemstone
25 Roman general
27 Country bumpkin
29 Spiny plant
30 Maintain
31 Wide
32 Nobleman's estate

DOWN

2 Nasal tone
3 Domestic cock
5 Greek letter
6 Perplex totally
7 Foam
8 Corkwood
9 Card-game
14 Brass instrument
16 Obstruct
18 Haven
20 State capital of Washington
21 Dance in triple time
23 Intermission
24 Laziness
26 Bear-like animal, zoo favourite
28 City of central Japan

ACROSS
1 Chewy sweet
4 Is aware of
8 Easily understood
9 Not many (anag.)
10 Made safe
11 Lowest part of ship
12 Skill
14 Unadorned
15 Fury
18 Globe
21 Naturalness
23 Facsimile
25 Atone
26 Homeric epic
27 Large spoon
28 Dramatically contrived

DOWN
1 Counter of votes
2 Magenta flowering plant
3 The golden land (2,6)
4 Hawklike bird
5 Wild cat
6 Specimen
7 Police car
13 Silent Cistercian
16 Sliding smoothly
17 Revoke
19 Produce offspring
20 Filled with stuffing
22 Savoury
24 Wise man

169

ACROSS

1 Quicken one's pace
4 Acted as leader
7 Church of see
9 Small particle
10 Ill-humour
11 Lose consciousness
13 Remove from text
14 Wish otherwise
15 Hunted victim
17 Route
19 Unintelligent person
20 Be up against
22 Final
23 Learning
24 Merchant
25 Take away

DOWN

1 Require forcibly
2 Smile broadly
3 Breathe out
4 One who avoids decision
5 Fine horse
6 Fault
7 Fellow
8 Keeper of volumes
11 Violent rain
12 Former Argentine leader
15 Daintily odd
16 Over there
17 Barrow-seller
18 Whole
21 Walked heavily
22 Weaving machine

170

ACROSS
1 Let fall
5 Regulate in a row
8 Part of flower
9 Not informed of
10 Not to be frightened
12 Marriage portion
13 Cycling
14 Champagne (sl.)
17 Conifer
18 Rudely aggressive
20 Early
21 Of the city
23 Cede
24 Watered down

DOWN
1 Tricked
2 Dismissed
3 Artist's colour-board
4 Coarsely painted
5 Accumulate
6 Can't be heard
7 "Keep out" (2,5)
11 She escorts to seat
13 In friendly way
15 Out of the ordinary
16 Tended
18 Faint-hearted
19 Adjusted musical pitch
22 Small boring tool

171

ACROSS

1 Collier
4 Error
8 Cane syrup
9 Poplar tree
10 Vassal
11 Wycliffe follower
13 Playthings
15 Beat harshly
17 Chief
20 Russian religious picture
22 University official
24 Vagrant
26 Squeeze
27 Violently cruel
28 Ambushed
29 Greatly fear

DOWN

1 French seaman
2 Female relative
3 Fraudulent businesses
4 With submissiveness
5 Play for time
6 Lover of Heloise
7 Remove errors
12 Scandinavian capital
14 American state
16 Bird colony
18 Attracted
19 Slept
21 Felt hunger for
22 Tropical fruit
23 Puccini opera
25 Without company

ACROSS
1 Small gastropod
4 Distrust
8 Ascended
9 Eye specialist
10 Group in statuesque pose
11 Low temperature
12 Weep
14 Giant
15 Scottish islet
18 Female rabbit
21 Scurry
23 Slow tempo
25 Small crown
26 Large jugs
27 Precipitous
28 Black Sea port

DOWN
1 Moderate heat
2 Horse-food container
3 Green lid (anag.)
4 Percussion piece
5 Join
6 Military pageant
7 Spurious
13 Convolvulus
16 Own up
17 Summary of a text
19 Planet
20 Iran's former name
22 Worsted cloth
24 Photograph

173

ACROSS

1 Downgraded
7 Attempt
8 Learning
9 Period
10 Stoned fruit
11 Victor
13 Flush
14 Uproar
17 Ancient (3-3)
18 Soft mass
20 Part of circumference
22 Conclusion
23 Sprout
24 Went round, evaded

DOWN

1 Great fear
2 On horseback
3 Greedy
4 Strong tincture
5 Large daisy
6 Nightwear
7 Lure into trap
12 Advantage
13 Backslide
15 Roman first of month
16 Downy
17 Thespian
19 Rough woollen cloth
21 Operatic air

174

ACROSS

1 Hunting-dogs
4 Trench
8 Lustrous ductile solid
9 Hastened
10 French porcelain centre
11 Lake
12 Large deer
14 Passage to mine
15 Simple
18 Recede
21 Part of foot
23 Distinctive nature
25 Fairy queen
26 Mediterranean fruit
27 Unpleasant
28 Fraud

DOWN

1 Lowly
2 Wild
3 Representative
4 Venture
5 Moment
6 Concealed
7 Pursue
13 Apex of arch
16 Dawn
17 Fingerless glove
19 Commenced
20 Seemly
22 Quotes
24 Covetousness

175

ACROSS

1 Drunken nightmares
5 Goods vehicle
8 Old French coin
9 One ostracised
10 Pirate's gibbet
11 Blood-sucking worm
12 Unwavering
14 Starting place
17 Holy memento
19 Withdraw
22 Call out
23 Subcontinent
24 Push with elbow
25 Take over strain

DOWN

1 Sharp-leaved tree
2 Setback
3 Greek letter
4 Tempestuous
5 A gossip
6 Tsarist edict
7 Cooking room
12 Operating physician
13 State firmly
15 Iberian nobleman
16 Elementary text-book
18 Strengthened with spirits
20 Patterned fabric
21 Feudal nobleman

176

ACROSS

1 Dull and clumsy
4 Give consent (3,3)
7 Wild bitter fruit (4,5)
9 Gloom
10 Dash
11 Nimble
13 Wish for
14 Restrained
15 Whiten
17 A shave
19 Two-masted vessel
20 Board game
22 Confined
23 Highly delighted
24 Cower
25 Diminutive

DOWN

1 Bored by wood beetles
2 Sinister
3 Marriageable
4 Evening meal
5 U.S. university
6 Added one's name
7 Getting louder (mus.)
8 Dangle toe (anag.)
11 Garment
12 Instruct
15 European sea
16 Funeral car
17 Shoal of fish
18 Complete
21 Baking chamber
22 Dried bog vegetation

177

ACROSS

1 Norfolk lake
4 Unwavering looks
9 Release dog
10 Michaelmas daisy
11 Deposit of ore
12 Copy
13 Animal skin
14 Encourage
16 Divisible by two
18 Hindrance
20 Break-up of marriage
21 A returning sound
24 Very big
25 Ancient war vehicle
26 Smartly attired
27 Unrelenting

DOWN

1 Cheap decoration
2 Stared lasciviously
3 Uninterestingly dull
5 One who defames
6 Go back over
7 Thoroughfare
8 Very steep
13 Brave
15 Change direction completely
17 Gone bad
18 Grey-barked tree
19 Sewing thread
22 Set of bells
23 Young girl

ACROSS
1 Snake
4 Appendix
8 Betrayer
9 Constellation
10 Chess piece
11 Mean
13 Manipulated
15 Insignia
17 Riddle
20 Bone of forearm
22 Hamlet
24 Not suited
26 Inanimate object
27 Make more attractive
28 In Leeds (anag.)
29 Cries loudly

DOWN
1 Old fashioned
2 Male duck
3 Attendant following
4 Red cherry colour
5 Quaintly amusing
6 Room's upper surface
7 Meal
12 Paradise
14 Self-satisfied
16 Precious metal in mass
18 Ill-behaved
19 Stage player
21 Mythical tale
22 Indispensable
23 Debate
25 Concluding

179

ACROSS

7 Impresses
8 Incentive
10 Linnet-like bird
11 Of Italy's capital
12 Triumphal building
13 Take oath
17 Exhausted
18 Fencing stake
22 Thick digit
23 Golf club
24 Unpretentious
25 A beginner

DOWN

1 Frugal type
2 Cross-valley bridge
3 Bend low
4 Dear Sim (anag.)
5 Group
6 Give a handslap
9 Coming into bloom
14 Wordy
15 Tranquil
16 Shouted speaker down
19 Receipt for postage
20 Pilot
21 Loathe

ACROSS
5 Illumination
8 With verve
9 Tale
10 Deerlike ruminant
11 Float aimlessly
14 Electric flash
16 Disclose
17 Holiday centre
18 Non-clerical
20 Resentment
24 Straight upwards
25 Buffalo
26 Physically strong
27 Card game

DOWN
1 Literary composition
2 Humorous
3 Young mare
4 Anger
6 Return on capital
7 Breed of cattle
12 Satanic
13 Cloud-like
14 Everyone
15 Weep
19 Street
21 Pile
22 Solo oar
23 Wide awake

181

ACROSS

1 Copper coin
4 Fantastic
8 Colouring substance
9 Trademark
10 Valued
11 Abhorred
13 Smoothe
15 Took long steps
17 Cot
20 Forest growth
22 Hair treatment
24 Sizzled
26 Miss Doolittle
27 Par
28 Part of doorlock
29 Braid of hair

DOWN

1 Paper-reed
2 Darkness
3 Gave in
4 Glass container
5 Striped horse
6 Arrived at
7 Concluded
12 Formerly
14 Power of rejecting
16 Verity
18 Ponder
19 Eternal
21 Turn like wheel
22 Cut of beef
23 Musical instrument
25 Wrathful

ACROSS

1 Mooring device
4 Pens
7 Chief
9 Owl's cry
10 Midday
11 Catlike carnivore
13 Decayed
14 Dell
15 Vertical support
17 Lapwing's family
19 Registers
20 Climb steeply
22 Stalk
23 Of course
24 Begrudged
25 Banishes

DOWN

1 Bowman
2 Injured
3 Going bad
4 Relinquished claim
5 Persia
6 Attitude
7 Post-boy
8 Long life
11 Evergreen conifer
12 Cultivates
15 Perplex
16 Round
17 Gratify
18 Negligent
21 Wise men of the East
22 Slight mistake

183

ACROSS
5 Viper
8 Pleasure seeking
9 Sacred song
10 Wedding
11 Linger
14 Eccentric
16 Inexperienced
17 Surpass
18 Of humble rank
20 Bedeck
24 Room heater
25 Deficient
26 Innkeeper
27 Binge

DOWN
1 Extreme suffering
2 Narcotic flower
3 Peel off
4 Looked pleased
6 Give death-blow to
7 Made greater
12 Hindrance
13 Man's name
14 Nocturnal bird
15 Natural moisture
19 Not transparent
21 Search and rob
22 Orderly pile
23 Edge

ACROSS
1 Foreman of ship's crew
4 Straits
8 Variety turn
9 Elector
10 Island in the Ionian Sea
11 Atlantic country
13 Ceremony
15 Surpass
17 Several
20 Uniform, smooth
22 French painter
24 Pleasanter
26 Resort in Florida
27 Underground cell
28 Asylum
29 Burn on surface

DOWN
1 Pedal vehicle
2 Staid, temperate
3 Bring up
4 Blockhead
5 Theatrical show
6 Atrocious act
7 Paring, ragged strip
12 Give way
14 15th or 13th day of month in ancient Rome
16 Small house
18 Spell at wicket
19 Injecting instrument
21 Seller
22 Childhood disease
23 Rapid
25 Washed

185

ACROSS
- **7** Floor
- **8** Bank clerk
- **10** Set free
- **11** Happening
- **12** Head cook
- **13** Lawful
- **17** Celebration
- **18** Anxiety
- **22** West African river
- **23** Public vehicle
- **24** Esteemed
- **25** Unassuming

DOWN
- **1** Flightless bird
- **2** Large stone
- **3** Mercenary
- **4** Army commander
- **5** Smooth and glossy
- **6** Angry
- **9** Choice
- **14** Wed
- **15** Took a risk
- **16** Thickness
- **19** Rascal
- **20** Nimble
- **21** Irritate

ACROSS

1 Originator
5 Set down
8 Old Testament book
9 Item of property
10 Downtrodden
12 Chart
13 Tuber
14 Courage
17 Bony pike
18 Word-book
20 Friendly
21 Spine of plant
23 Stratum
24 Tiny fish

DOWN

1 Indian ascetic
2 Large vessel
3 Sweet course
4 Small opening
5 Tartan fabric
6 Height gauge
7 Interception of light
11 Fatherhood
13 Braid of hair
15 Passed as law
16 Not long ago
18 Roman river
19 Spanish title
22 Nocturnal bird

187

ACROSS
1 Calling on
7 Herb
8 Well-timed
9 Anger
10 Parched
11 Selection
13 General standard
14 Root vegetable
17 Brides (anag.)
18 Crustacean
20 Cereal
22 Comfortable seat (4,5)
23 Rub down a horse
24 Lucid

DOWN
1 Pansy-like flower
2 Young tree
3 Horse-racing world
4 Cipher
5 Eagle's nest
6 Expand
7 Irksome
12 Difficulty
13 General standard
15 Tell a story
16 Complete disaster
17 Deceptive stratagem
19 Exploded
21 Land measurement

ACROSS

1 Mark Twain's Tom
4 Leguminous plants
8 Wild animal
9 Travelling bags
10 Breaks the phone call (4,3)
11 Stoop
12 Drudgery
14 Abominable snowman
15 A liturgy
18 Chalice
21 Yielding
23 Conflagration
25 Careful watch
26 Fetters
27 Enid Blyton character
28 Firearm

DOWN

1 Dapper
2 Pare with a knife
3 Run at a profit
4 Entreats
5 Informed
6 Swift
7 Soft down
13 Wall scribblings
16 Evict (4,3)
17 Small falcon
19 Devoutness
20 Of the back
22 Chide
24 Small bunch of flowers

189

ACROSS

1 Vital organ
4 Boy's name
9 Devoted
10 Delicate silk fabric
11 Trick
12 Hibernating
13 Busy insect
14 Finished
16 Marble-like mineral
18 Title
20 Equivalent word
21 Rancid
24 Portion out
25 Rotate
26 Gloss paint
27 Elbow

DOWN

1 Pitfall
2 Accumulate
3 Weight system for gold, etc
5 Outside
6 Cradle song
7 Votes into office
8 Privately
13 Dark-haired female
15 Flavouring essence
17 Manor
18 Clever
19 Light wind
22 Lubricated
23 English river

ACROSS

7 Give up, abandon (4,2)
8 Television (3,3)
10 Agreement
11 Of the nose
12 Dutch cheese
13 Arm-joint
17 Painful muscular spasm
18 Closed
22 Throng of insects
23 Fishing-vessel
24 Collect
25 Basque ball game

DOWN

1 Dismissed, turned out
2 Injury to reputation
3 River in Italy
4 Spectre
5 Abnormally fat
6 Rejoice exceedingly
9 Deadlock in chess
14 Brass instrument
15 Garlic flavoured onion
16 Everlasting
19 Custom, treatment
20 Rashly quick
21 French composer

191

ACROSS

1 Prayer before meal
4 Term of endearment
8 Hold down
9 Handed over
10 Avoid
11 Not prepared
13 Relaxation
15 Mislead
17 Polish capital
20 Porridge
22 Edible berry
24 Puzzle
26 Biblical queen
27 Research chemist
28 Perceive
29 Cogs

DOWN

1 Flower-wreath
2 Sufficient
3 Thrown out
4 Athlete's disc
5 Fast car
6 Cowboys and —
7 Suffering from vertigo
12 Small salamander
14 Very long period
16 Bountiful charity
18 Road-surface material
19 Australian shrub
21 Reach
22 Surveyed by burglars
23 Quickly
25 Distinctive manner

ACROSS
7 Withstand
8 Posture
10 Coarse aggregate
11 Pastoral
12 Ballet skirt
13 Unobscured
17 Belief
18 Alcoholic drink
22 Split in two
23 Prudent
24 Numeral
25 Red Indian tribesman

DOWN
1 Commendation
2 Set apart
3 Evaluation of gold, etc
4 Never-ending
5 Infuriated
6 Cathedral city
9 His cattle (anag.)
14 Cake or wine
15 Flawless
16 Wheeled carrier
19 Stealing
20 Sad poem
21 Burst forth

193

ACROSS

1 Rod or cane
4 Crude
7 Supporting beam
9 To name
10 Christmas
11 Trifle with love
13 Staid
14 Tested for flavour
15 Apportions
17 3-D sound?
19 Speedy
20 Destiny
22 Stride
23 Leader writer's piece
24 Having tassels
25 Arctic language

DOWN

1 Cut thinly
2 Art gallery
3 Manipulate
4 Band of warriors
5 West of England river
6 Early geometrician
7 Incite
8 By night
11 Foam
12 Ragged and shabby
15 To influence
16 Seasoned
17 Give no food
18 Act excessively
21 Prepare for printer
22 A bundle

194

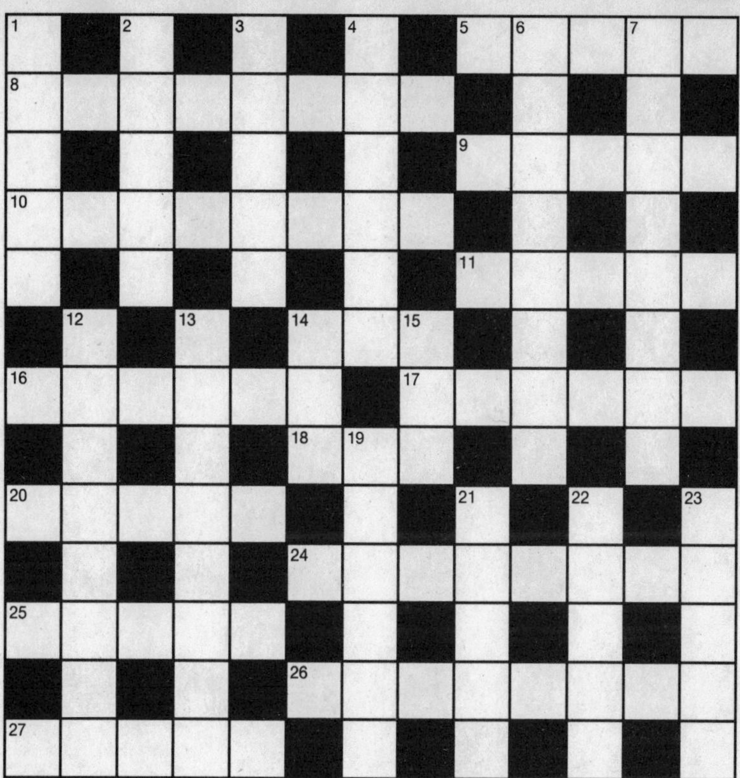

ACROSS
5 Fireplace
8 Needs laundering
9 Look intently
10 Next day
11 Cereal
14 Piece of weaponry
16 Mediterranean island
17 Tree-lined road
18 Dried grass
20 Part of a wicket
24 Insolvent
25 Evidence
26 Carry on
27 Shelter

DOWN
1 Hearty enjoyment
2 Marshland
3 Seize illegally
4 Eat voraciously
6 Sent back
7 End of the line
12 This year (anag.)
13 Spring flower
14 Residue
15 Tree
19 Great river
21 Flatfish
22 Amusing
23 Freshwater animal

195

ACROSS

1 Theatrical poster
7 Enclosed areas near buildings
8 Spanish cavalier
9 Fish
10 Nimble
11 Quality that raises pity
13 Wooden villa
14 Spectre
17 Pay up
18 Cautious
20 Ingest
22 Venetian boatman
23 Tree with oily fruit
24 Daring

DOWN

1 Agreements
2 Province of Canada
3 Arrow
4 Sideways drift of boat
5 Steep rugged rocks
6 Largest living bird
7 Milk-food
12 Surviving trace
13 King Arthur's legendary site
15 Think
16 Momentary look
17 Sober, sedate
19 Long tales
21 Make fast a ship

196

ACROSS

1 Prohibited
4 Lord
7 Pre-eminent
9 One of several rows
10 Transaction
11 Hinder
13 Awakens
14 More expensive
15 Tar
17 Chaff
19 Nautical
20 Feathered missile
22 Short nail
23 Recent past
24 Divine drink
25 Flag

DOWN

1 Pancake mixture
2 Close
3 Curtains
4 Docked
5 Dispatch
6 Hair curler
7 Relating to money
8 Land
11 Devil
12 Royal
15 Abrupt
16 Roof beam
17 Scottish playwright
18 Blush
21 Trial
22 Deep male voice

197

ACROSS

1 Dressed in
5 Be of value to
8 Subject of discourse
9 To the purpose
10 Great sorrow
12 Old prophet
13 Column
14 Rotter (coll.) (3,3)
17 Beast
18 Pub worker
20 Take back
21 Leg bone
23 Ragged strip
24 Water main connection

DOWN

1 Lookout
2 Expert
3 Passivity
4 Deflect
5 Concur
6 Arrest
7 Putting into catalogue
11 Big American reptile
13 Paper-reed
15 Gave alarm
16 Tree fork
18 Provision of meals
19 Bake
22 Feathered neck piece

198

ACROSS
1 Small
4 Sound of bell
8 Legally acceptable
9 Business controller
10 Departing
11 Extent
12 Finish
14 Gala
15 Peruse
18 Vital juice
21 Impetuous
23 Adhered (anag.)
25 Epicure
26 Top people
27 Darkness
28 Revolve

DOWN
1 Beautiful
2 Husbandry
3 Machine wreckers
4 Considerate
5 Keen
6 Lasso
7 Idol
13 Uninteresting toil
16 New World
17 Fabulous monster
19 Talk foolishly
20 Stick
22 Oscillated
24 Black mark

199

ACROSS

1 Mans a ship
4 Object thrown
8 Lengthen
9 Doorkeeper
10 English river
11 Shameful
13 Paradise
15 Formal prayer
17 Relative (fam.)
20 Takes sustenance
22 At home
24 Fit out
26 Dutch pottery town
27 Behind time
28 Organise
29 Varieties

DOWN

1 Investment funds
2 Call up
3 Abridge
4 Chattering bird
5 Rebuff
6 Populate
7 Nest of an eagle
12 Insect
14 One who colours fabrics
16 Child learning to walk
18 Of no avail
19 Imperial title
21 On dry land
22 Asian republic
23 Regularly
25 Beneath

ACROSS
1 Cabriolet
4 Tree-cutter
7 Semaphore operator
9 Writer of verse
10 Antlered animal
11 Fast
13 Go to bed
14 Absentee from school
15 Brief instant
17 Bracket candlestick
19 Eskimo canoe
20 Surgical dressing
22 U.S. army vehicle
23 Three-month term
24 Tried
25 Zero

DOWN
1 Picnic basket
2 Piece of burlesque
3 Mix
4 Cut of meat
5 German song
6 Feeling of sorrow
7 Emotion
8 Whatever is left
11 Honest
12 Goods vehicle
15 Annoy vexatiously
16 Book of Jewish law
17 Proverbial strong man
18 Sends goods overseas
21 Slow canter
22 Fast driver

201

ACROSS

1 Monstrous bird-woman (myth.)
4 Spiritualist agent
9 Sickly-sentimental
10 Oral
11 Vein of ore
12 Not distinct
13 Affected dandy
14 Slightly open
16 Dull and dismal
18 Take to court
20 Dose of medicine
21 Lateral branch
24 Prop
25 Tract
26 Trader's property
27 Gloomy

DOWN

1 Lowly
2 Circular
3 Shout
5 Consider
6 Take in
7 Wood hammer
8 Pry
13 Unfinished portion
15 Have green eyes?
17 Black Sea port
18 Thieved
19 Volcano mouth
22 Leguminous seeds
23 Magician's rod

ACROSS

1 Brought up
3 Desserts
9 Shakespearean lover
10 Nuclear pile
11 45 inches
13 Pertaining to midwifery
14 Treeless plains
16 Purloined
18 Washerwoman
20 Word of affirmation
22 Frigidity
23 Ritual washing basin
25 Stored wealth
26 Main stalk

DOWN

1 Canal vessel
2 Tree
4 General disturbance
5 Local language
6 Without affectation
7 Crusader's opponent
8 Song for one voice
12 Luxurious car
14 Hand-reader
15 Formal speech
17 Stretching muscle
19 Fine sediment
21 Pluck strings aimlessly
24 Large barrel

203

ACROSS

7 Go-between
8 Register
10 One spiritually changed
11 Small flat scale
12 Necessity
13 Mild and soothing
17 Drink
18 Covered
22 Meditate moodily
23 Trip
24 Croaky call
25 Mean

DOWN

1 Flee from the law
2 Barrister
3 Horizontal plane
4 Fragrance
5 Type of bear
6 Snake
9 Resolute
14 End of the day
15 Strike hard (sl.)
16 Additions
19 Bottomless gulf
20 Sham
21 Amusing

ACROSS

1 Shut
4 Wicker containers
8 Not public
9 Clad with stones
10 Unit of heat
11 Fervent
13 Exploited
15 Edible grasshopper
17 Vitreous
20 Superficial extent
22 Get ready
24 Israelite leader
26 Avoid
27 Method of bowling
28 Attracted
29 Pinch with a twist

DOWN

1 Chief city
2 Oil-producing fruit
3 Dutch scholar
4 Light wind
5 Reddish-brown
6 Resentful
7 Teams
12 Border
14 Heavenly body
16 Merciful
18 Softly radiant
19 Muslim veil
21 Gramophone disc
22 Flat dish
23 Room under roof
25 Agitate

205

ACROSS	DOWN

ACROSS

5 A jury
8 Sufferance
9 Range
10 Indian war-axe
11 Skirmish
14 Tree
16 Ridiculous
17 Clamour
18 Short swim
20 Small bird
24 Mishap
25 Very bright
26 Big shop
27 Senseless

DOWN

1 River-flood
2 Die mark
3 River in Hades
4 Sullen looks
6 Precise
7 Imposter's unmasking
12 Forgetfulness
13 Social gathering
14 Put on
15 Dancing party
19 Revenue
21 Guide
22 Danger
23 Staunches

ACROSS

1 Performer on ice
4 Bullet
8 First in rank
9 Turned
10 Ejected from home
11 French cheese
12 Consume
14 Queen of the gods
15 Conceal
18 Auction item
21 Water plant
23 Cockerel
25 Inhabited
26 Extend arm
27 Scolded
28 Declared

DOWN

1 Late meal
2 Foolish
3 Final
4 Ceremony
5 Speak
6 Evaded
7 Classification
13 Deified ruler
16 Take away from
17 Correct
19 Commerce
20 Exquisite flower
22 Spirit drink
24 Clothed

207

ACROSS
1 More substantial
5 Correct
8 Brutishly wild
9 Women
10 Judge
11 Japanese American
12 Parent
14 Wandering cattle
17 Indian address
19 Descent
22 Resident physician
23 Sightless
24 Greeting
25 One who betrays

DOWN
1 Criminal gang
2 Display gymnast
3 Small island
4 Remove defects
5 Calls to thought
6 Fierce winds
7 Give evidence
12 Jewish deliverer
13 Ban
15 Pragmatist
16 Customer
18 Residential establishment
20 Nile region
21 Senior church member

208

ACROSS

1 Scrutineer
5 Wearied by tedious talk
8 Wedlock
9 Real bun (anag.)
10 Strong verbal attack
12 Male swan
13 Ill repute
14 Equilateral rectangle
17 Bribe given to mollify
18 Lawyer
20 Deny
21 Mythological king bound to a wheel
23 Offspring of tiger and lioness
24 Sewing instruments

DOWN

1 Morsel of food
2 O.T. priest
3 Realm
4 French painter
5 Sacred book
6 Unwilling
7 Hardy
11 Children
13 Penetrative understanding
15 Substance used formerly to treat malaria
16 Chalk-pencil
18 Hollow depression
19 Letters of ancient Germanic alphabet
22 Sick

209

ACROSS
5 Beneath
8 Status
9 Type of chalcedony
10 Render shockproof
11 Pebble
14 Primate
16 Not so bad
17 Survey
18 Rocky height
20 Deathly pale
24 Enjoyment
25 Wading-bird
26 Meant
27 Drinking vessel

DOWN
1 On the move
2 Heart's-ease
3 Grown-up
4 Part of foot
6 Implying "No"
7 Prolonged
12 Private
13 Tries
14 Cunning
15 Sin
19 Lubricating
21 Tag
22 Pal
23 Out of sorts

210

ACROSS

1 High-ranking officers
7 Strap for corporal punishment
8 Musician
9 Mesh
10 Challenge
11 Small stone
13 Cereal plant
14 Ancient Greek coin
17 Surgical stitch
18 Leave out
20 Equipment
22 Water reserve
23 Rule as monarch
24 Buried

DOWN

1 Confined to college
2 Uncommitted
3 Engrossed
4 Rubbish
5 String
6 Colonist
7 Words of approbation
12 Reading desk
13 Derision
15 Drum
16 Gaol
17 Narrow band
19 Exhausted
21 Unbound

211

ACROSS
1 Dramas
4 Bring into accord
9 Requisite
10 Northern sea-duck
11 Swirl
12 Pain-relieving drug
13 Strange
14 Rebuke
16 Eagerly excited
18 Pale
20 Debar
21 Close
24 Scene of combat
25 Cattle thief
26 Scatter
27 Harvest

DOWN
1 Fastened
2 Correct
3 Secure
5 Actor
6 Experience
7 Commission
8 Implore
13 Stubborn
15 Kernel
17 Messenger
18 Uncanny
19 Gazed
22 Divide by 2
23 Observe

ACROSS

5 Communicate by letter
8 Draw near
9 Aggregate
10 Dig out
11 Unfresh
14 Novel by Haggard
16 Famous canal
17 Expressing views
18 Equal value
20 Tiny particles
24 Letter holder
25 Roof tile
26 Subterranean story
27 Jousting weapon

DOWN

1 Stories
2 Emptiness
3 Find answer
4 Whisky
6 Cockerels
7 Dragging behind
12 Spanish scarf
13 Ceremonial cloak
14 Plant juice
15 Hearing organ
19 Yearly
21 Diseased outcast
22 Swain
23 Very slowly

213

ACROSS

1 Pestered persistently
7 Useless plants
8 Watchfulness
9 Tawny
10 Reluctant
11 Garden flower
13 Pleasantly odd
14 Cream-cake
17 Series of steps
18 Great multitude
20 Tear
22 Coastal region of W. Ireland
23 Foe
24 Almanac (4-4)

DOWN

1 Wretched dwelling
2 Boat-race meeting
3 Q.C.'s gown
4 Set of nine things
5 Greek letter
6 Into parts
7 Matrimony
12 Childhood
13 Breach of friendship
15 Tropical fruit
16 EEC country
17 Amphetamine (sl.)
19 Express gratitude
21 Shakespearean king

ACROSS
7 Indian social classes
8 Cut loose
10 Threatening
11 Corner
12 Memorandum
13 Sorceress
17 Corpulent
18 Portent
22 Irrigate
23 Futile
24 Attitude
25 Squirm

DOWN
1 Descriptive report
2 Helps
3 Criminal
4 Go forward
5 Scorch
6 Horse
9 Diligent
14 Catch the eye
15 General pardon
16 Flavour of ouzo
19 Contort
20 Book of maps
21 Joyous

215

ACROSS

1 Gun-dog
4 Restrict
8 Become void through time
9 Eager in love
10 Shutting
11 List of courses
12 Finish
14 Irritation
15 Left-overs
18 Also
21 German wine
23 Language of Flanders
25 Brief rest
26 Cease-fire
27 Assassinated Egyptian leader
28 Agree

DOWN

1 Comfort
2 Highest
3 Vision
4 Weaving machine
5 American elk
6 Soft paper
7 Canine disease
13 Pertaining to the home
16 Speech of praise
17 Refrain of song
19 Frequently
20 Ripened curd
22 Looked over with criminal intent?
24 Strike coins

ACROSS

1 Rumpled roughly
5 Channel port
8 Infectious illness
9 Scrutinised
10 Backstage worker
11 Subject of essay
12 Criminal maiming
14 Worshipped
17 Concede
19 e.g. Blackcap, whitethroat
22 Sharply
23 Himalayan kingdom
24 Upright
25 Most profound

DOWN

1 Domesticated
2 Ridiculous ceremonial
3 Misplaces
4 Abandon
5 Called in question
6 Give utterance
7 Copper-haired
12 Man of wealth and power
13 Ask earnestly
15 Fall back
16 Vacillated
18 Sky blue
20 Wash out lightly
21 Ignited again

217

ACROSS
5 Refuge
8 Advance
9 Item of property
10 Native of Yerevan
11 Australasian serviceman
14 Sheltered side
16 Tenant
17 Foresight
18 An era
20 Postponement
24 Wolfhound
25 Belt
26 Avid reader
27 Has weapons

DOWN
1 Horrify
2 Punctuation mark
3 Stamp with hot iron
4 Run away
6 Pyromaniac
7 Mechanical lift
12 Defector
13 Irresponsible undertaking
14 Measure of yarn
15 First woman
19 Unit of capacity
21 Sticky
22 Stubborn believer
23 Foe

218

1		2		3	■	4		5		6		7
	■		■		■		■		■		■	
8							■	9				
	■		■		■		■		■		■	
10					■	11	12					
	■	■	■	13	14			■	■		■	■
15		16				■	17	18				19
■	■		■	■	20	21			■	■	■	
22				23			■	24		25		
	■		■		■		■		■		■	
26					■	27						
	■		■		■		■		■		■	
28							■	29				

ACROSS
1 Precious stone
4 Aim
8 Regal heirs
9 Culpability
10 Royal House
11 Fatness
13 African river
15 Noise
17 Result
20 Heal
22 Vertical
24 Come again
26 Fruit
27 Make ready
28 Mock-orange
29 Rhythm

DOWN
1 Planet
2 Eerie
3 Swiss lake
4 Firearm
5 Rascal
6 Opening
7 Way in
12 Beverage
14 Irritation
16 Pirate
18 Earnest
19 Poor Ted (anag.)
21 Ideal state
22 Prevails upon
23 Colour
25 Amulet

219

ACROSS

1 Ship's officer
4 Mistakes
9 Nine-sided figure
10 Male member of religious order
11 Endure
12 Humanity
13 Timid
14 Small flute
16 Sicilian volcano
18 Command
20 Voter
21 Ignoble
24 Joined links
25 Prevailing weather
26 Stinging plant
27 Praise

DOWN

1 Bracelet
2 Dispatches
3 Near
5 Paid money back
6 Personal belief
7 Long step
8 Foe
13 Sentry
15 Imprecise
17 Signal fire
18 Pair
19 Expose
22 Separate
23 Conceal

ACROSS

1 Entire
4 Mariners
8 Cooking area
9 River in Pakistan
10 Sacked
11 Tambourine
13 Want
15 August 1
17 Editorial
20 Encounter
22 Sparkle
24 Detests
26 Bury
27 Stresses
28 Well-bred
29 Tresses

DOWN

1 Vigilant
2 External
3 Spiny ant-eater
4 Upper chamber
5 Peculiarity of speech
6 Commanded
7 Agave fibre
12 Unemployed
14 Girl's or boy's name
16 Slightly wet
18 Moral
19 Opposes
21 Necessitate
22 Norwegian composer
23 Concise
25 Pick-me-up

221

ACROSS
1 Arrange in row
4 Intended
10 Road surface
11 Acquiesce
12 Delicate fabric
13 Low platform
15 Police spy
17 Sweetmeat
19 Urge forward
22 British composer
25 Inhale
27 Noosed rope
29 Form
30 Ancestry
31 Small-minded
32 Cathedral city

DOWN
2 Village inn
3 Windfall
5 Precise
6 Tell story
7 Metal worker
8 Yellowish orange
9 Smooth
14 Dermis
16 Indian nanny
18 Unexceptional
20 Medley
21 Degrade
23 Kingdom
24 Pith helmet
26 English river
28 Diminutive

ACROSS
1 English county
5 Boat-race crew
8 Chief citizen
9 Clump of grass
10 Go along with
12 Zodiac sign
13 Getting up
14 Distant (3,3)
17 Insect
18 Committed to memory
20 Door appendage
21 Lasso
23 Cheerless
24 Attentive

DOWN
1 Syncopated dance
2 Aviate
3 One of 5 across
4 Soldier's luggage (3-3)
5 Written composition
6 Handsome appearance (4,5)
7 Skit (4-3)
11 Oven dish
13 Chided
15 Put in order
16 Sully
18 Fabricator
19 Reside
22 Away

223

ACROSS

1 Hungarian composer
4 Clergyman
7 Eternal punishment
9 Musical work
10 Valley
11 Hair on chin
13 Horse-attendant at inn
14 Pamphlets
15 Place for instruction
17 Washed lightly
19 Adult females
20 Mus. symbol indicating pitch
22 Expel
23 Wires
24 Score
25 Refusal

DOWN

1 Japanese robe
2 Word expressive of grief
3 Over there
4 Witty answer
5 Stupid fellow
6 Horsemen
7 Cloth for protecting furniture (4-5)
8 Bulbous, spring flower
11 Elbow (anag.)
12 Exhaust
15 Unrevealed
16 Extremely beautiful
17 Brought up
18 Relate minutely
21 Bracken
22 Prophetic sign

ACROSS
1 Hellenic
5 Has no doubt
8 Signifies
9 Large, thick-set dog
10 Strict
11 Head of State
12 Impassive
14 Catch-phrase
17 Ease up
19 Rebellious
22 Deep in thought
23 Minute piece of bread
24 Eat away
25 To the same degree

DOWN
1 Letter of Greek alphabet
2 Pleased (anag.)
3 Matter in dispute
4 Figure
5 Small falcon
6 Oxford college
7 Orange-yellow colour
12 Misgiving
13 Woven material
15 Step-by-step
16 Stick to
18 Musically slow
20 Frilly neckwear
21 Plump

225

ACROSS

1 Call together; revive
4 Killed by immersion
8 Grassy plain
9 Piece of glowing wood
10 Offspring
11 Snuggled closely
13 Harvest
15 Enter services
17 Small islands
20 Notch
22 — and Isolde
24 Instil, inspire
26 Sky-blue
27 Deliberate insult
28 Go before
29 Tree

DOWN

1 Repeat of earlier theme
2 Loiters idly
3 Bowling deliveries
4 Chaperon
5 Portents
6 Faint, misty star-clusters
7 Ventured
12 Long heroic poem
14 Volcano in Sicily
16 Free time
18 Accomplished
19 Doubter
21 Enter by military force
22 Vagrant
23 In that place
25 Grill

ACROSS

1 Restrains
4 Anagram of 5
10 According to rule
11 Splendid
12 Shelf
13 Purveyed foods
15 Contended
17 Rate
19 Pedestrian crossing
22 German song
25 Traversed
27 Overturn
29 Scandinavian goblin
30 Unyielding
31 Concur
32 Bunk

DOWN

2 Exhorted
3 Regard as true
5 Attack
6 Largest of penguins
7 Gridiron
8 Vestige
9 Haughtiness
14 Axe with arched blade
16 Lazy
18 Extend
20 Teach
21 Sharp
23 Perfect
24 Condition
26 Ointment
28 Begin

227

ACROSS
1 Highways
4 Neckband
9 Greenery
10 Rub out
11 Tidings
12 Reprieve
13 A pair
14 Not quick
16 Border
18 Container
20 Tongue of bell
21 Unemployment money
24 Flavour
25 Merchants
26 Leased
27 Attire

DOWN
1 Part repayment
2 Permit
3 Chair
5 Supervised
6 Bias
7 Staggered
8 French underground
13 Woman's suit
15 Contact between allies
17 Sea-duck
18 Commonplace
19 Animals
22 Overweight
23 Pasteboard

ACROSS

1 Put money into bank (3,2)
4 Conjectured
8 Not suitably
9 Headless trunk
10 Render void
11 Ginger things up
13 Unbleached linen
15 Portuguese coin
17 Bright garden flower
20 Chain of rocks
22 Bed covering
24 Natural aptitude
26 Confinement in oblivion
27 Set apart
28 Unhappiness
29 Lock of hair

DOWN

1 Common soldier
2 Long for
3 Stung
4 Hot water spring
5 Praise highly
6 Dry up
7 To flood
12 Unclothed
14 Central part
16 Entranced
18 Open insult
19 Stuffy
21 Science of morals
22 Takes hurried flight
23 Norwegian silver piece
25 Open-mouthed

229

ACROSS

1 Single combat
3 Governs
9 Columnar statement
10 Shown off
11 Coal-scuttle
13 Will
14 Pertain
16 Shouted
18 Acknowledge
20 Rainy
22 Panther
23 Manufacturer
25 Permanent inhabitant
26 Round handle

DOWN

1 Trench
2 Decline
4 Resist
5 Row of houses
6 Benevolent society member
7 Given a tranquilliser
8 Zone e.g. Green
12 Delightful
14 Housebreaker
15 Miser
17 Concealed
19 Jane Austen novel
21 Pulsate
24 Relatives

230

ACROSS
1 Loftier
4 Mistrust
8 Cook in oven
9 Listless
10 Succinct
11 Semi-precious stone
12 Young goat
14 Not working
15 Military force
18 Animal
21 Classic race
23 Yacht race-meeting
25 Gleam
26 Dance
27 Portion
28 Light wind

DOWN
1 Obstacle
2 Looked briefly
3 Lengthened
4 Completed
5 Seize illegally
6 Childish walk
7 Courage
13 The guard (anag.)
16 Afternoon show
17 Spin a coin (4,2)
19 Welcome
20 Coax
22 Court card
24 Scottish isle

231

ACROSS
5 Tired out
8 Protective surface
9 Zest
10 Renew
11 Hirsute
14 Mimic
16 Opening to admit light
17 Made good
18 Go astray
20 Merry-making
24 Dealer in precious stones
25 Pick me up
26 Take away
27 Yellowish grey colour

DOWN
1 Twenty
2 Happening
3 Indian warrior
4 Part of foot
6 Teacher
7 Gave sharp answer
12 Wearisome
13 Sticking
14 Reverential fear
15 Listener
19 Sorry
21 Biters
22 Implore
23 Beast of a man!

ACROSS

1 Brood
4 Narrow street
8 Hackneyed
9 Impure
10 Atone
11 Lake
12 Tear
14 Boy's name
15 Prevalent
18 Urge
21 Hasty
23 Venerated
25 Feeling
26 Branch that means peace
27 Symbol
28 View

DOWN

1 Epistle
2 Excursionist
3 Grace
4 Roguish
5 Vassal
6 Over there
7 Monarch
13 Former
16 Stealthy
17 Clergyman
19 Magnificent
20 Coming
22 Unpleasant surprise
24 Bearing

233

ACROSS

1 Portion
4 Creator
10 Friendly
11 Take place
12 Sharp bend
13 Shrove Tuesday fare
15 Thoroughfare
17 I.Q. club
19 Consent
22 Paired dwelling
25 Specialists
27 Pretty girl
29 Ward off
30 Erotically indifferent
31 *Sotto voce* remark
32 Theatre attendant

DOWN

2 Cake-covering
3 Mates
5 Furnish with ornaments
6 Territory hemmed in
7 Formal address to woman
8 The common wasp
9 Firs, oaks, etc
14 First human
16 Hop-drying kiln
18 Non-stop
20 Esculent organs of bird
21 Relieve tension
23 Literary composition
24 Stringed instrument
26 Scolded
28 Parasitic insect

ACROSS
1 Genealogy
7 Yachting centre
8 Mass
9 Take to court
10 Pile
11 Enthusiast
13 Stone-fruit
14 On beach
17 Yellow/green finch
18 Back a horse
20 Intimidate
22 Of high quality
23 Beneath
24 Obliged by a favour

DOWN
1 Fish illegally
2 Deprive of office
3 Narrow valley
4 Vitrified surface
5 Warp yarn
6 Slander
7 Big violin player
12 Kitchen sideboard
13 Go to pieces (5,2)
15 Luxuriant
16 Gem-like mineral
17 Scandinavian
19 Carried
21 Depressed

235

ACROSS
1 Pugilist
5 Unadorned
8 Coalition
9 Souvenir
10 Lured
11 Twangy
12 Lighterman
14 Enumerates
17 Hooded snake
19 Gap
22 Tasteless
23 Unaccompanied
24 Kind
25 Vacillates

DOWN
1 Accidental success
2 Sparkle
3 Pick-me-up
4 Cure
5 Allspice
6 Girl's name
7 Simpletons
12 Support
13 Instance
15 Objectionable
16 Squalid
18 Bowl
20 Precise
21 Conjecture

ACROSS

7 Thespian art
8 Complete agreement
10 Malaria antidote
11 A saying
12 Test (abbr.)
13 Supplies
17 Spite
18 Heavenly body
22 Freshwater fish
23 Small onion
24 Large drinking cup
25 Renowned

DOWN

1 Feast
2 Morally correct
3 Sluggish mollusc
4 Childhood
5 Short composition
6 Glossary
9 Luxury top-flat
14 Tanned hide
15 Kind of cheese
16 Complain
19 Raised platform
20 Pastime
21 Colourful parrot

237

ACROSS

5 Protect from danger
8 Gathering of women only (3-5)
9 Abnormally fat
10 Announce officially
11 The true skin
14 Beverage
16 Roll in mud
17 Edible leaf-stalk
18 Dismissed in cricket
20 Port of Southern Sweden
24 Hour-glass (3-5)
25 Foot-lever
26 Hollowed-out design in gem
27 Lean forward

DOWN

1 Lashes
2 Combination, concord
3 Reassemble
4 Dress
6 Portable protection from rain
7 Fragrant herb
12 Saucy, forward
13 Graphite
14 Deuce at cards
15 Play part
19 Pressing
21 Wander away
22 Narrow part of back
23 Constellation

ACROSS

1 Status
7 Catarrh
8 Gross disrespect
9 Perceive
10 Smooth
11 Retract
13 Move up and down
14 Recompense
17 Rogue
18 Declines
20 Fuss
22 Quack
23 Verify
24 Wavered

DOWN

1 County
2 Stern, harsh
3 Puppet
4 French town
5 Leaven
6 Hindered
7 Akin
12 Pillage
13 Slight wound
15 Judge
16 Summer hat
17 Wild West show
19 Church assembly
21 Blemish

239

ACROSS

1 Hot season
4 Aperients
8 Fast car
9 Towing vehicle
10 To what place?
11 Dull impact
12 Spoil
14 Ban
15 Simple
18 Space
21 Church recess
23 Intensely hated
25 Great stream of water
26 An Indian language
27 Water-lily
28 Took notice of

DOWN

1 Scattered
2 Mechanical tool
3 Aardvark
4 Hit with open hand
5 Door fastener
6 Long step
7 Tempest
13 Witty retort
16 Plotted
17 Drawing chalk
19 Flat dish
20 Gone bad
22 Brace
24 Spandau inmate

ACROSS

1 Back-lane
4 Ankle covering
9 Grassy plain
10 Scope
11 Quaintly pleasing
12 Close associate
13 Clamour
14 Festivity
16 Swelling
18 Climbing plant
20 Hail with applause
21 Guy
24 Adhered to
25 Worthless matter
26 Brood of kittens
27 Symbol

DOWN

1 Silken wool cloth
2 Inclined
3 CID HQ
5 Bitterness
6 Large mug
7 Stank
8 Coppers
13 Pompous address
15 Statement
17 Package
18 Idol
19 Winged monster
22 Express gratitude
23 Courage

THE ANSWERS

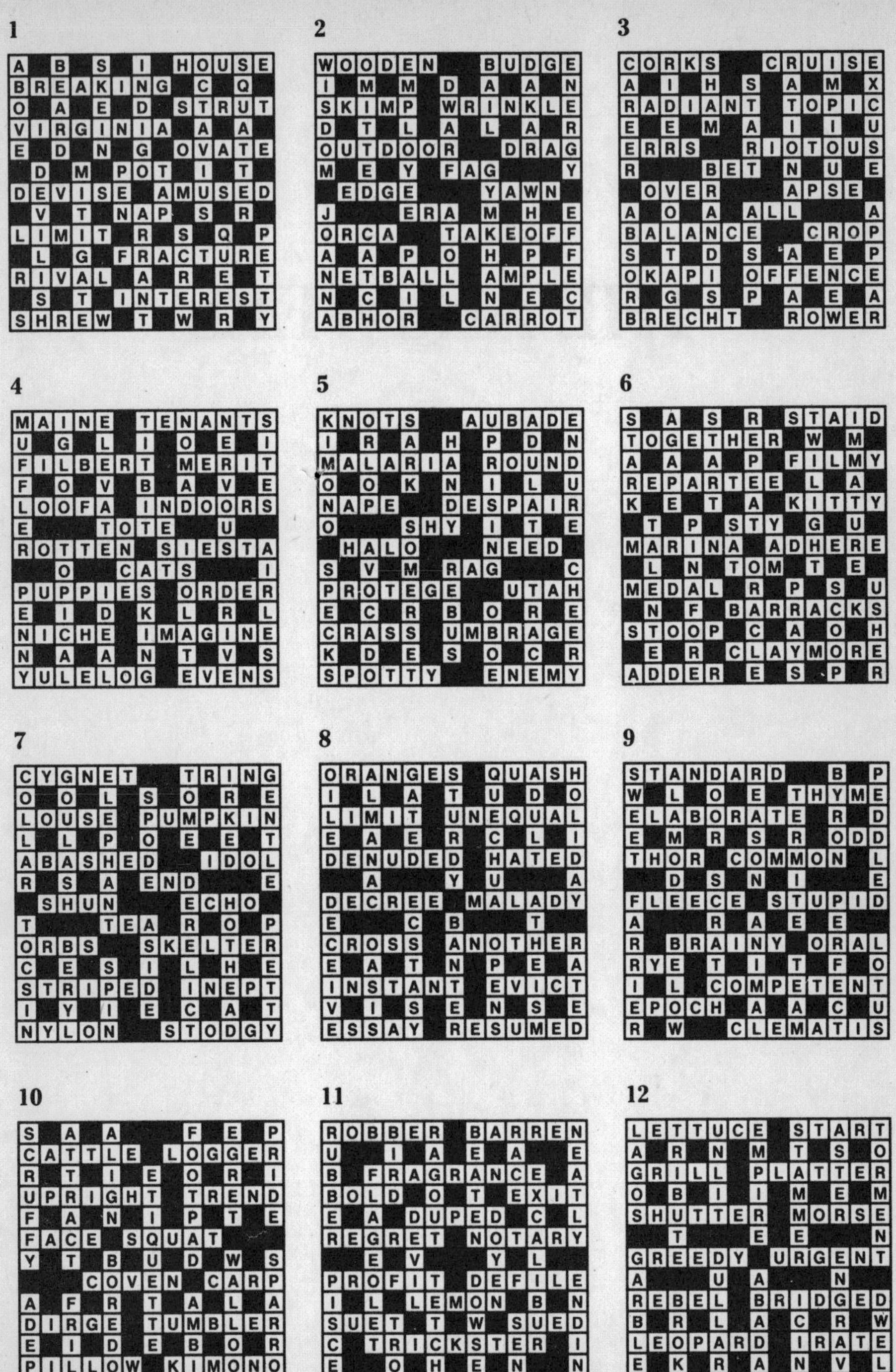

13

J	U	S	T	I	C	E		W	E	I	G	H
U		I		L		S		H		N		A
I	M	P	E	L		T	H	I	N	N	E	D
C				I		E		S		O		D
E	F	F	I	C	I	E	N	T		C	O	O
		R		I		M				U		C
G	A	I	E	T	Y		U	N	C	O	R	K
E		T				S		E		U		
S	E	T		L	A	W	L	E	S	S	L	Y
T		E		A		I		D				I
U	P	R	I	G	H	T		L	O	I	R	E
R		E		E		C		E		L		L
E	I	D	E	R		H	U	S	T	L	E	D

14

V	E	I	N		G	L	O	R	I	O	U	S
I		N		H		O		E		U		A
T	E	N	S	E		N	E	G	A	T	E	D
A				A		E		R		S		N
L	I	P		P	U	L	V	E	R	I	S	E
		R				Y		T		D		S
P	L	E	A	S	E		A	S	S	E	S	S
O		C		E		M				R		
P	O	L	I	S	H	I	N	G		S	E	W
U		U		S		N		A				I
L	O	D	G	I	N	G		S	W	A	R	D
A		E		O		L		P		D		E
R	E	S	E	N	T	E	D		S	O	O	N

15

S	C	E	N	T		P	A	C	K	I	N	G
H		N		E		E		L		N		R
A	T	T	E	M	P	T		E	N	S	U	E
L		E		P		I		A		T		E
L	A	R	G	E		T	A	N	K	A	R	D
O				S	T	E	P			N		
T	O	M	A	T	O		E	A	S	T	E	R
		I			T	E	X	T				E
C	O	L	O	N	E	L		L	I	G	H	T
U		L		I		E		A		U		I
P	A	I	N	T		V	E	N	I	S	O	N
I		O		R		E		T		T		U
D	U	N	G	E	O	N		A	B	O	D	E

16

	M	I	N	E	R		Q	U	A	Y	S	
S		N		A		L		V		A		S
C	H	E	L	S	E	A		U	P	S	E	T
O		R		E		P		L		H		O
P	A	T	I	O		S	T	A	M	M	E	R
E				F	L	E	A			A		K
	D	A	F	F	Y		C	H	O	K	E	
S		B			R	A	T	E				S
P	A	R	A	P	E	T		R	O	A	S	T
E		I		O		L		R		L		A
E	N	D	O	W		A	L	I	M	E	N	T
D		G		E		S		N		R		E
	W	E	I	R	D		A	G	A	T	E	

17

S	H	E	A	R		T	O	R	T	U	R	E
E		L		U		H		A		T		N
C	R	E	V	I	C	E		T	H	E	M	E
U		C		N		L		E		N		M
R	A	T	I	O		M	O	D	E	S	T	Y
E				U	T	A	H			I		
D	E	M	I	S	E		M	E	R	L	I	N
		A			L	A	S	T				U
A	S	S	A	U	L	T		E	P	S	O	M
E		S		L		T		R		O		B
S	W	I	F	T		I	G	N	O	B	L	E
O		V		R		R		A		E		R
P	R	E	S	A	G	E		L	U	R	E	S

18

S		C		F				P		A		A
P	R	O	F	I	T		M	A	R	G	I	N
A		N		L		P		R		A		G
R	U	S	T	L	E	R		A	L	I	V	E
T		E		Y		O		G		N		R
A	R	N	E		I	G	L	O	O			
N		T		H		R		N		R		B
			J	A	P	A	N		T	E	A	R
Q		S		R		M		E		L		I
U	T	T	E	R		M	I	G	R	A	N	T
A		R		I		E		G		T		I
R	E	A	P	E	R		R	E	C	E	S	S
T		D		R				D		D		H

19

S	M	A	S	H	I	N	G			P		D
I		M		I		E		T	H	Y	M	E
S	C	A	V	E	N	G	E	R		L		F
A		Z		D		A		E		O	A	R
L	A	I	D		S	T	A	M	E	N		A
		N		G		E		B				U
B	E	G	G	A	R		P	L	A	C	I	D
L				R		A		E		O		
A		U	N	M	A	D	E		A	N	T	!
N	A	P		E		H		M		C		S
K		P		N	E	E	D	I	N	E	S	S
E	V	E	N	T		R		N		R		U
T		R			S	E	N	T	E	N	C	E

20

M	A	K	E	R			L	I	V	I	N	G
U		R		U		M		O		M		E
F	R	A	G	I	L	E		L	U	P	I	N
F		I		N		R		A		E		T
I	O	T	A			G	E	N	E	R	A	L
N				F	O	E		T		I		E
	F	A	L	L				H	A	L	E	
A		R		A		S	E	E				M
F	O	R	E	M	A	N			G	A	L	A
F		I		I		I		P		S		L
R	I	V	E	N		D	R	A	C	H	M	A
A		A		G		E		C		E		D
Y	E	L	L	O	W			T	E	S	T	Y

21

K	N	I	G	H	T			T	E	A	S	E
A		N		A		S		A		L		N
R	A	V	E	N		P	A	C	K	A	G	E
A		O		D		A		T		R		R
T	W	I	N	S	E	T			S	M	U	G
E		C		O		S	A	G				Y
	B	E	A	M				A	L	L	Y	
C				E	F	T		R		I		D
L	I	F	T			A	U	D	I	B	L	E
A		A		J		R		E		E		S
R	E	B	O	U	N	D		N	U	R	S	E
E		L		S		Y		I		A		R
T	R	E	N	T			B	A	L	L	E	T

22

D	I	S	C		C	U	S	H	I	O	N	S
E		E		C		N		O		T		I
M	A	T	C	H		K	I	T	C	H	E	N
U				I		I		F		E		L
R	I	P		C	O	N	C	O	U	R	S	E
		L				D		O		W		S
D	E	A	R	T	H		S	T	A	I	R	S
R		Y		E		F				S		
I	N	T	E	N	T	I	O	N		E	N	D
F		H		U		N		U				U
T	R	I	P	O	L	I		M	E	A	N	S
E		N		U		T		B		N		K
R	E	G	I	S	T	E	R		S	T	A	Y

23

S		C		R				M		A		F
P	R	O	P	E	R		G	A	N	D	E	R
A		N		A		L		G		A		I
R	E	S	I	D	U	E		E	X	P	E	L
K		O		Y		V		N		T		L
L	U	L	L		M	I	R	T	H			
E		E		C		T		A		D		I
			T	O	N	I	C		H	E	L	M
S		S		M		C		O		F		I
C	H	A	S	M		U	P	S	T	A	R	T
A		L		E		S		I		M		A
L	O	V	I	N	G		D	E	F	E	C	T
E		E		T				R		D		E

24

C	O	V	E	R			C	H	A	R	G	E
L		A		I		B		I		A		N
I	M	P	R	O	V	E		G	O	N	E	R
E		I		T		L		H		T		A
N	O	D	E			L	A	G	G	I	N	G
T				A	P	E		A		N		E
	F	L	A	N				T	U	G	S	
A		I		A		C	U	E				H
C	R	A	W	L	E	R			F	L	E	A
C		I		Y		O		A		A		N
O	A	S	I	S		W	O	R	S	T	E	D
R		O		I		N		M		H		E
D	A	N	I	S	H			S	T	E	A	L

25

```
CROSS WHIRRED
H V P E D E I
ELEVATE INFER
R R R V O I G
OUTER IMMENSE
O   OILY  E  
THROWN RANDOM
  E  CRAM   A
BLANCHE ANTIC
L L H S T I B
ALIBI TRESTLE
S S L E U A T
TUMBLED RANCH
```

26

```
 SWINE HEARD 
A A A P S E P
GESTURE SUGAR
I T G R E A I
LEECH IGNORED
E   TILE  D E
 STAYS ABYSS 
S R  LORE   S
CREEPER GUILT
O M U G G R E
REBEL ANIMATE
E L S N N T P
 DEFER AGREE 
```

27

```
STRANGLE  B A
O E E O HOLED
LASSITUDE A A
I I L V M DIM
DODO GRILSE A
  U T E O   N
SEETHE ACCEPT
T   O P K R  
R FRUGAL JUNK
EWE G R R D N
T R HARMONICA
COAST O O T V
H L  STAMPEDE
```

28

```
HAVOC  UPPITY
O I L L R M E
MOORAGE ORIEL
A L M N G T L
GRAB  TORNADO
E   ZOO E T W
 ISLE   STEP 
S T P ASS   C
CRAMPED  SKUA
O R E E P R R
RAVEL PROFANE
C E I T O A E
HIDING  RULER
```

29

```
V A S S PLANE
ENVELOPE A O 
R O O A SCENT
GLITTERS E S 
E D H E GREET
 M D ODD A N 
JOVIAL ARTIST
 L S DIM E E 
DEBAR C T O W
 S S RESOLUTE
STATE B K T I
 E E COLANDER
ADORN X Y O D
```

30

```
BRIDLE  SWEET
O N A F I Q U
ROTOR LANGUID
A R G E K A O
GRUYERE  SLUR
E D S TIE   S
 MESS   SATE 
C   ELM T W M
ARCH  ADIPOSE
R O G R M S N
TIPPLER ABOUT
O E U Y T M O
NUDGE  METEOR
```

31

```
SETTER SIGHED
L  O O A O  O
E PRESIDENT T
UGLY A D GUST
T O BRILL R E
HOURLY EARNED
  G A   R T  
ACHING PREACH
S M DAILY B A
SCAB M I BLOT
A NAVIGABLE R
I  R N N E  E
LAPDOG TIDIED
```

32

```
COLE SHORTAGE
H O G E U N X
ACTOR CABINET
R   I A B U E
MOA METHEGLIN
  M   E R M D
IRONED ASSESS
S R X M   N  
HAPHAZARD TOP
M H M N A   E
ADORING ROBOT
E U N L E A T
LESSENED TRAY
```

33

```
WHINE GLASSES
A N V R L E C
RAGTIME TITLE
B O D E E S N
LITRE NARRATE
E   NEST  I  
RARITY OUTLAW
  E ELMS    E
COLLIDE EXTRA
L I S S L I L
AMASS SLEIGHT
S N U O S E H
PATTERN STRAY
```

34

```
PENNY  TRAITS
A E A T E N A
REGULAR SUGAR
A U E U E R O
DESK  TERRAIN
E   ASH V T G
 WORM   EWER 
E C E AID   I
STENTOR  WREN
T A H G S H V
HANDY OUTLINE
E I S N A N R
RECITE  GHENT
```

35

```
HAMMER  SMITH
A A L B I T I
WORSE REDUCED
S R P O E H D
EPITHET  TYPE
R E A HAT   N
 ODIN   ROCK 
G   TAN U A D
EDDY  IGNOBLE
Y A T G C I A
SELFISH ANNUL
E L L T T E E
ROYAL  BETTER
```

36

```
CHURCH WARDEN
U  O U E E  E
T PLUNDERER E
TIRE T V DEED
E E DEVIL P E
ROTTER LEERED
  E B   V I  
TORRID SERMON
A I TOPER A A
BETA N A SNAG
L EXHAUSTED G
E  L T O E  E
DELETE NIPPED
```

37

```
E#A#P###J#F#A
MOSQUE#EATERS
E#E#N#P#N#N#P
REPLICA#UNCLE
A#T#C#R#A#E#N
LAIR#STERN###
D#C#F#R#Y#M#O
###PLAID#MAIM
F#A#U#D#S#T#I
LIGHT#GYMNAST
E#E#T#E#I#D#T
CINDER#ORIOLE
K#T#R###K#R#D
```

38

```
STANDIN#GROOM
L#U#O#O#R#V#E
ORDER#BRADAWL
P#I#I#O#N#T#O
ENTICED#AMEND
##O###Y###R#I
PORTER#MYOPIC
L###V#B###R##
AGREE#APTNESS
S#A#R#N#R#S#A
TRIDENT#ALERT
I#S#S#A#I#N#Y
CREST#MONITOR
```

39

```
SMOKER##SCOFF
O#M#V#C#A#L#E
OUNCE#RUFFIAN
T#I#N#A#E#V#N
HABITAT##MERE
E#U#U#ELK###L
#ASIA###AIDA#
L###LET#N#E#B
INCH##ALGEBRA
M#H#L#N#A#A#N
PROLONG#RACED
E#S#U#O#O#L#I
TWEED##HONEST
```

40

```
FERVOUR#MOORE
A#U#U#E#O#U#X
COMET#SCUTTLE
E###R#C#S#S#R
SIGNATURE#PIG
##O#G#E###O#U
GIBBET#PICKLE
E#E###S#N#E##
NET#IMPUDENCE
E#W#T#A#U###A
STEWARD#LUNAR
I#E#L#E#G#A#L
SUNNY#SHEPPEY
```

41

```
FARE#EXCHANGE
A#A#A#E#O#A#N
TUTOR#RELATED
A###G#X#S#U#O
LOG#OVERTHROW
##R###S#E#I#E
TRAJAN#ERASED
O#D#N#C###T##
BLUNTNESS#SAW
A#A#W#L#A###A
COLLECT#LOTUS
C#L#R#I#E#A#T
OLYMPICS#BRIE
```

42

```
OVERT##EARNED
U#N#I#S#L#A#I
TITANIC#DRILL
I#E#T#O#E#V#U
NORM##PERFECT
G###TOE#M#T#E
#USER###APEX#
W#T#A#PAN###C
ETERNAL##ARIA
B#P#S#U#L#A#N
BESOM#CAUTION
E#O#I#K#N#S#O
DENOTE##GREEN
```

43

```
S#C#S#K#WHINE
MERCHANT#E#O#
I#A#A#I#EDITH
RIFFRAFF#G#I#
K#T#K#E#DELFT
#S#D#ADD#H#I#
CARESS#RIOTER
#P#B#PLY#G#D#
SPRAY#U#C#H#S
#H#R#IMPUDENT
MITRE#B#R#N#U
#R#E#LESSENED
HEADY#R#E#A#Y
```

44

```
METTLE##PLATE
O#I#A#W#O#R#X
ATTIC#AUSTERE
N#U#E#G#T#N#T
ENLARGE##VANE
D#A#A#RIG###R
#FRET###RAGE#
G###EAR#A#E#S
IOWA##UNDERGO
F#A#H#L#I#M#R
TILLAGE#ELAND
E#T#Z#R#N#N#I
DIZZY##STAYED
```

45

```
A#S#A###C#A#P
MAKING#RHODES
A#I#N#X#A#E#A
TILBURY#REPEL
E#L#L#L#I#T#M
USED#COLON###
R#T#S#P#T#C#M
###MIGHT#POLO
S#H#L#O#S#N#N
WHALE#NETTING
I#V#N#E#E#F#R
FRESCO#BREEZE
T#N#E###N#R#L
```

46

```
SPECK#TICKLES
L#A#I#O#A#O#I
ANTONYM#CANON
N#E#S#A#H#G#U
DENIM#TRELLIS
E###ALOE##E##
RAVINE#SLIGHT
##A##FETE###O
MAGENTA#OSIER
A#R#E#S#T#C#M
GRASP#TRAPEZE
U#N#A#E#R#N#N
SETTLER#DRIFT
```

47

```
CHIMNEYS##S#E
O#N#O#E#TACKS
VIRTUALLY#A#S
E#O#S#L#R#RUE
NEAR#HORACE#N
##D#C#W#N###C
LESION#ENTIRE
E###R#D#Y#N##
A#MADDEN#SCAR
TIE#I#N#S#L#E
H#R#ADVENTURE
ENROL#E#I#D#D
R#Y##FRIPPERY
```

48

```
MISTER#CHANCE
A###A#E#H#B#F
S#SLANDERED#F
TEAK#O#E#DENE
E#T#SWORD#A#T
RAISIN#SARTRE
##S#N###R#H##
COFFER#BEDLAM
O#I#WADED#E#O
BEET#N#A#ASIA
B#DANGEROUS#T
L###S#E#E#T#E
ERASER#ROOKED
```

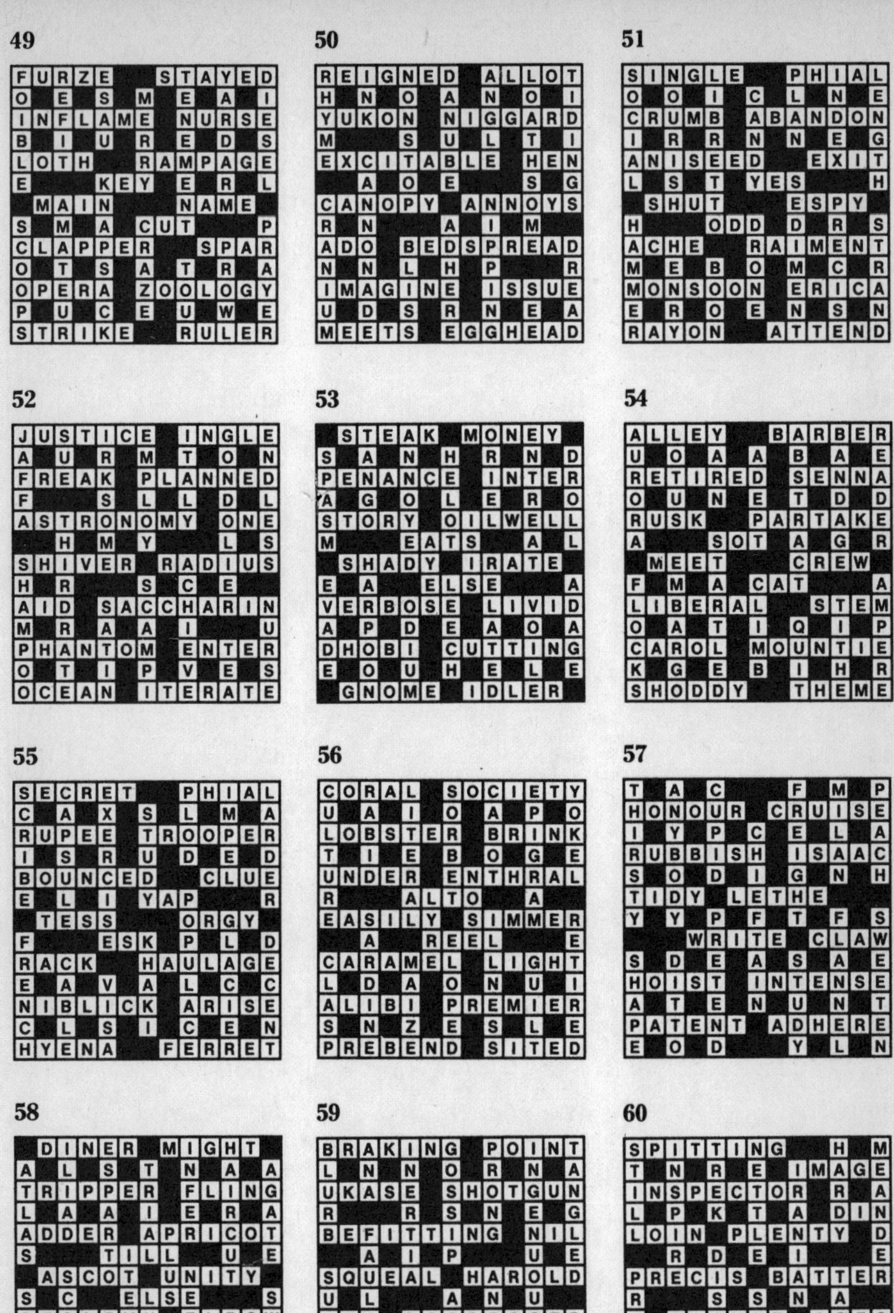
49
FURZE STAYED
O E S M E A I
INFLAME NURSE
B I U R E D S
LOTH RAMPAGE
E KEY E R L
MAIN NAME
S M A CUT P
CLAPPER SPAR
O T S A T R A
OPERA ZOOLOGY
P U C E U W E
STRIKE RULER
50
REIGNED ALLOT
H N O A N O I
YUKON NIGGARD
M S U L T I
EXCITABLE HEN
A O E S G
CANOPY ANNOYS
R N A I M
ADO BEDSPREAD
N N L H P R
IMAGINE ISSUE
U D S R N E A
MEETS EGGHEAD
51
SINGLE PHIAL
O O I C L N E
CRUMB ABANDON
I R R N N E G
ANISEED EXIT
L S T YES H
SHUT ESPY
H ODD D R S
ACHE RAIMENT
M E B O M C R
MONSOON ERICA
E R O E N S N
RAYON ATTEND
52
JUSTICE INGLE
A U R M T O N
FREAK PLANNED
F S L L D L
ASTRONOMY ONE
H M Y L S
SHIVER RADIUS
H R S C E
AID SACCHARIN
M R A A I U
PHANTOM ENTER
O T I P V E S
OCEAN ITERATE
53
STEAK MONEY
S A N H R N D
PENANCE INTER
A G O L E R O
STORY OILWELL
M EATS A L
SHADY IRATE
E A ELSE A
VERBOSE LIVID
A P D E A O A
DHOBI CUTTING
E O U H E L E
GNOME IDLER
54
ALLEY BARBER
U O A A B A E
RETIRED SENNA
O U N E T D D
RUSK PARTAKE
A SOT A G R
MEET CREW
F M A CAT A
LIBERAL STEM
O A T I Q I P
CAROL MOUNTIE
K G E B I H R
SHODDY THEME
55
SECRET PHIAL
C A X S L M A
RUPEE TROOPER
I S R U D E D
BOUNCED CLUE
E L I YAP R
TESS ORGY
F ESK P L D
RACK HAULAGE
E A V A L C C
NIBLICK ARISE
C L S I C E N
HYENA FERRET
56
CORAL SOCIETY
U A I O A P O
LOBSTER BRINK
T I E B O G E
UNDER ENTHRAL
R ALTO A
EASILY SIMMER
A REEL E
CARAMEL LIGHT
L D A O N U I
ALIBI PREMIER
S N Z E S L E
PREBEND SITED
57
T A C F M P
HONOUR CRUISE
I Y P C E L A
RUBBISH ISAAC
S O D I G N H
TIDY LETHE
Y Y P F T F S
WRITE CLAW
S D E A S A E
HOIST INTENSE
A T E N U N T
PATENT ADHERE
E O D Y L N
58
DINER MIGHT
A L S T N A A
TRIPPER FLING
L A A I E R A
ADDER APRICOT
S TILL U E
ASCOT UNITY
S C ELSE S
PTOLEMY ELBOW
I U N R D U E
TERSE INFIDEL
E G M C U G L
PEPYS FLEET
59
BRAKING POINT
L N N O R N A
UKASE SHOTGUN
R R S N E G
BEFITTING NIL
A I P U E
SQUEAL HAROLD
U L A N U
NET POSSESSED
R L S C M R
ITERATE ORATE
S S L N N R A
EPSOM DREAMER
60
SPITTING H M
T N R E IMAGE
INSPECTOR R A
L P K T A DIN
LOIN PLENTY D
R D E I E
PRECIS BATTER
R S S N A
E SICKLE ACES
DIP A U W T Y
I A RADIATION
CODED G K C O
T E RELEASED

61

P	A	S	T	U	R	E		E	X	A	M	S
A		N		S		A		N		C		I
R	O	U	G	H		R	E	C	I	T	A	L
C		G		E		T		H		O		E
H	O	G	A	R	T	H		A	P	R	O	N
		L				Y		N				C
S	K	E	W	E	R		S	T	A	B	L	E
H				A		A				R		
R	A	Z	O	R		C	H	A	R	I	O	T
I		O		R		C		M		S		E
V	A	M	P	I	R	E		B	A	K	E	R
E		B		N		P		L		E		S
L	Y	I	N	G		T	R	E	S	T	L	E

62

S		C		J				W		E		C
T	U	R	N	E	R		H	A	N	D	E	L
A		U		W		A		R		I		I
R	E	S	P	E	C	T		L	O	C	U	M
T		A		L		T		O		T		B
L	I	D	O		T	E	A	C	H			
E		E		Q		N		K		R		B
			S	U	I	T	E		R	I	L	L
S		E		A		I		D		P		E
C	O	V	E	R		O	N	E	R	O	U	S
A		E		T		N		M		S		S
M	A	N	N	E	R		L	U	S	T	R	E
P		S		R				R		E		D

63

C	H	A	R	R	I	N	G			P		I
A		V		A		O		C	R	O	S	S
T	R	A	N	S	P	I	R	E		K		O
C		R		P		S		N		E	L	L
H	E	I	R		B	E	T	T	E	R		A
		C		C		S		U				T
E	V	E	L	Y	N		P	R	A	I	S	E
X				A		L		Y		N		
A		P	U	N	T	E	R		A	C	H	E
M	A	Y		I		S		R		I		N
P		L		D	I	S	C	U	S	S	E	D
L	O	O	S	E		O		S		O		E
E		N			A	N	C	H	O	R	E	D

64

C	A	R	R	O	L	L		L	I	N	E	R
A		U		B		I		I		A		E
S	I	N	U	S		N	U	M	E	R	A	L
C				E		G		I		C		A
A	B	H	O	R	R	E	N	T		I	V	Y
		I		V		R				S		E
F	O	D	D	E	R		L	A	P	S	E	D
L		E				L		C		U		
A	L	B		H	E	Y	P	R	E	S	T	O
T		O		E		C		O				T
T	R	U	N	D	L	E		B	L	E	A	T
E		N		G		U		A		N		E
R	I	D	G	E		M	A	T	A	D	O	R

65

S	I	G	H	E	D		S	T	E	P	P	E
C		I		W		I		R				X
H		A	S	S	E	S	S	I	N	G		C
E	N	D	S		L		T		E	R	S	E
M		D		A	L	I	E	N		E		E
E	G	R	E	S	S		R	A	I	N	E	D
		E		S				T		A		
L	A	S	C	A	R		A	T	O	D	D	S
O		S		M	U	G	G	Y		I		E
I	D	E	A		B		R		A	N	T	E
T		D	I	L	I	G	E	N	C	E		T
E			M		E		E		R			H
R	A	I	S	E	S		D	R	E	D	G	E

66

C		A		S				P		A		A
H	I	G	H	L	Y		P	R	I	S	E	D
E		O		A		F		O		S		D
R	E	N	T	I	E	R		D	R	A	K	E
I		I		N		A		U		Y		R
S	A	S	H		S	T	U	C	K			
H		E		R		E		T		C		T
			B	E	A	R	D		P	O	O	R
S		B		S		N		T		N		I
T	R	A	I	T		A	S	I	A	T	I	C
O		N		O		L		A		E		K
R	E	D	U	C	E		B	R	U	N	E	L
Y		Y		K				A		T		E

67

W	R	I	T	E	R	S		R	E	I	G	N
A		C		X		T		U		L		E
S	W	E	E	P		A	I	R	F	L	O	W
T				U		T		A		N		M
E	S	S	E	N	T	I	A	L		A	D	O
		L		G		C				T		O
C	R	A	Z	E	D		R	E	T	U	R	N
H		P				D		N		R		
A	S	S		L	A	U	N	D	R	E	S	S
R		T		A		L		E				I
I	D	I	O	T	I	C		M	A	N	G	O
O		C		I		E		I		U		U
T	O	K	E	N		T	U	C	K	B	O	X

68

B	R	O	U	G	H	A	M			D		S
L		U		O		L		S	T	I	C	K
I	N	T	E	N	S	I	V	E		Z		I
N		C		E		G		C		Z	I	P
D	O	O	M		C	H	A	T	T	Y		P
		M		O		T		I				E
B	R	E	A	C	H		W	O	N	D	E	R
E				U		C		N		R		
Z		H	A	L	L	O	W		D	I	S	C
I	D	A		I		L		E		F		R
Q		R		S	A	L	T	P	E	T	R	E
U	P	S	E	T		I		E		E		E
E		H			D	E	F	E	R	R	E	D

69

F	A	I	R	S			P	L	E	A	S	E
O		M		K		H		A		M		L
R	E	P	L	I	C	A		C	E	A	S	E
E		E		M		P		R		T		C
S	I	L	K			P	R	O	T	E	C	T
T				S	P	Y		S		U		S
	E	D	I	T				S	I	R	E	
H		I		A		C	U	E				R
U	N	C	A	N	N	Y			F	R	E	E
M		K		D		C		I		O		V
O	M	E	G	A		L	E	T	T	U	C	E
U		N		R		E		E		N		A
R	E	S	I	D	E			M	O	D	E	L

70

A	L	L	O	W	E	D		N	O	Y	E	S
T		A		E		I		U		A		U
H	O	N	E	D		L	U	R	C	H	E	R
O		O		G		U		S		O		G
S	O	L	V	E	N	T		E	R	O	D	E
		I				E		R				O
M	E	N	A	C	E		P	Y	T	H	O	N
U				R		F				A		
S	P	U	M	E		R	E	S	E	R	V	E
T		P		V		A		W		I		R
A	M	P	L	I	F	Y		I	N	C	U	R
N		E		C		E		N		O		O
G	O	R	S	E		D	O	G	S	T	A	R

71

H	O	B	B	Y			H	O	A	R	S	E
A		I		A		V		B		E		S
M	I	N	E	R	V	A		S	I	F	T	S
P		G		N		U		O		R		A
E	V	E	R			L	U	L	L	A	B	Y
R				G	E	T		E		I		S
	R	O	L	E				T	I	N	Y	
K		M		N		A	X	E				P
E	V	I	D	E	N	T			P	U	M	A
E		N		R		O		S		L		R
P	H	O	T	O		L	I	N	C	T	U	S
E		U		U		L		I		R		O
R	E	S	I	S	T			P	L	A	I	N

72

B	U	T	T	E	R		M	O	M	E	N	T
A			O		O		A		E			A
N		S	O	J	O	U	R	N	E	D		T
G	U	L	L		T		I		T	E	X	T
O		A		M	E	A	N	T		L		L
R	E	P	A	I	D		E	R	M	I	N	E
		S		N				E		V		
T	I	T	H	E	S		S	N	E	E	Z	E
E		I		R	I	G	H	T		R		X
M	U	C	K		N		A		S	E	C	T
P		K	I	D	N	A	P	P	E	D		E
E			L		E		E		R			N
R	O	S	T	E	R		D	E	F	E	C	T

73

INTER SEEDING
R O E I L L R
KINSMAN VILLA
S G A G E N V
OKAPI LARCENY
M NOEL S
ENLIST TUSSLE
I TROT X
ICEFLOE EXULT
N D E D N B R
EPOCH RESTORE
P W A U I A M
TANTRUM LATHE

74

S G S U WHINE
MERCHANT A A
A A A I ANNUL
SEPARATE D T
H H E E ASTIR
R R ODE O C
REBUFF BOMBAY
L M FOB E L
PERIL S S T H
V N VICTORIA
BANAL R E U R
N T DIRECTED
STREW S P H Y

75

O C P C A S
DOUBLE FOUGHT
Y R E S N A E
SETBACK CHINA
S A D I E N M
EMIT SNARE
Y L A F T D D
STILL WISE
M Y T I A S E
OBESE NONSTOP
U A M T G A S
STRIPE CRINGE
E N T Y T A

76

MANNA WAUGH
P L O C I H S
LATERAL SHEEP
A E F O L R A
TORSO WRECKED
O LINE I E
POLKA ATONE
S V GAPE S
CHEVIOT MOIST
A R D T P N U
MODEL ICELAND
P U E C S N Y
WEIRD STEER

77

S A F C S B
METTLE WORKER
O T E S N I A
TORRENT SALON
H A T R O L D
EACH FIERY
R T M N T D F
RANGE ZERO
E S R E A C R
DETER NUMERAL
I A I T B I O
TAMPER VENEER
H P D R D N

78

SOLED SHORT
W T A L O U S
INTERNE REMIT
N E N H S M E
DIRGE AVERAGE
Y SORE G P
PASTA GAVEL
T L TRAP A
RELAPSE PYLON
I E A A A E G
PAGAN CARAMEL
E E I H E O E
EDICT SLANG

79

MUSTERED E A
A A S N CEDES
TRUMPETER I T
C N Y I O FIR
HATE STUFFY I
E A Y T D
CARAFE FEEBLE
O F M R U
C ADROIT AGES
KEG O N R B I
N R NEGLIGENT
ERECT L F A E
Y E DEFERRED

80

SUITE DREAMS
W C L S E N E
IMITATE POSED
T N N V R W A
CAGE EMINENT
H BAR S R E
EMMA APSE
C O R ILL T
OMNIBUS SLOE
M S A S E I R
FATED UNCOVER
I E O E H I O
THRASH ORDER

81

FOOLS RUSHING
E C U E I N L
DECORUM RIFLE
E U P O E E A
RURAL TANTRUM
A USED N
LOCUST ABROAD
O ACME E
ALLEGRO DRESS
N L I M R L S
DREAR PROMISE
E C T E O Z R
SATCHEL MEANT

82

S B S B A A
WELWYN TENDED
A A R M G U E
LECTURE ORLOP
L K P R N T T
ODER SCRIM
W N B E A M T
WRONG BIER
O B I A B N A
SPRIG REYNARD
C A A Y R R I
AMIENS MODERN
R D D N T G

83

ALLEY MONEY
B O A D R M H
ADVERSE DRAMA
R E N N E N S
GORSE SERVANT
E STEP T Y
PLATE EMBER
O A AREA S
FORSAKE TIGHT
F C L B I O E
EVENT UNNERVE
R N E T E G R
HYDRA SEVER

84

EIGHT BELLES
M L R S L O H
PROTECT ERASE
I S K O V F E
RASH REAGENT
E DAM T R S
STYE OUST
S E F AIR C
PERFECT MESH
R M A T G A I
IDIOT ILLEGAL
N T E C E L L
GREEDY EMERY

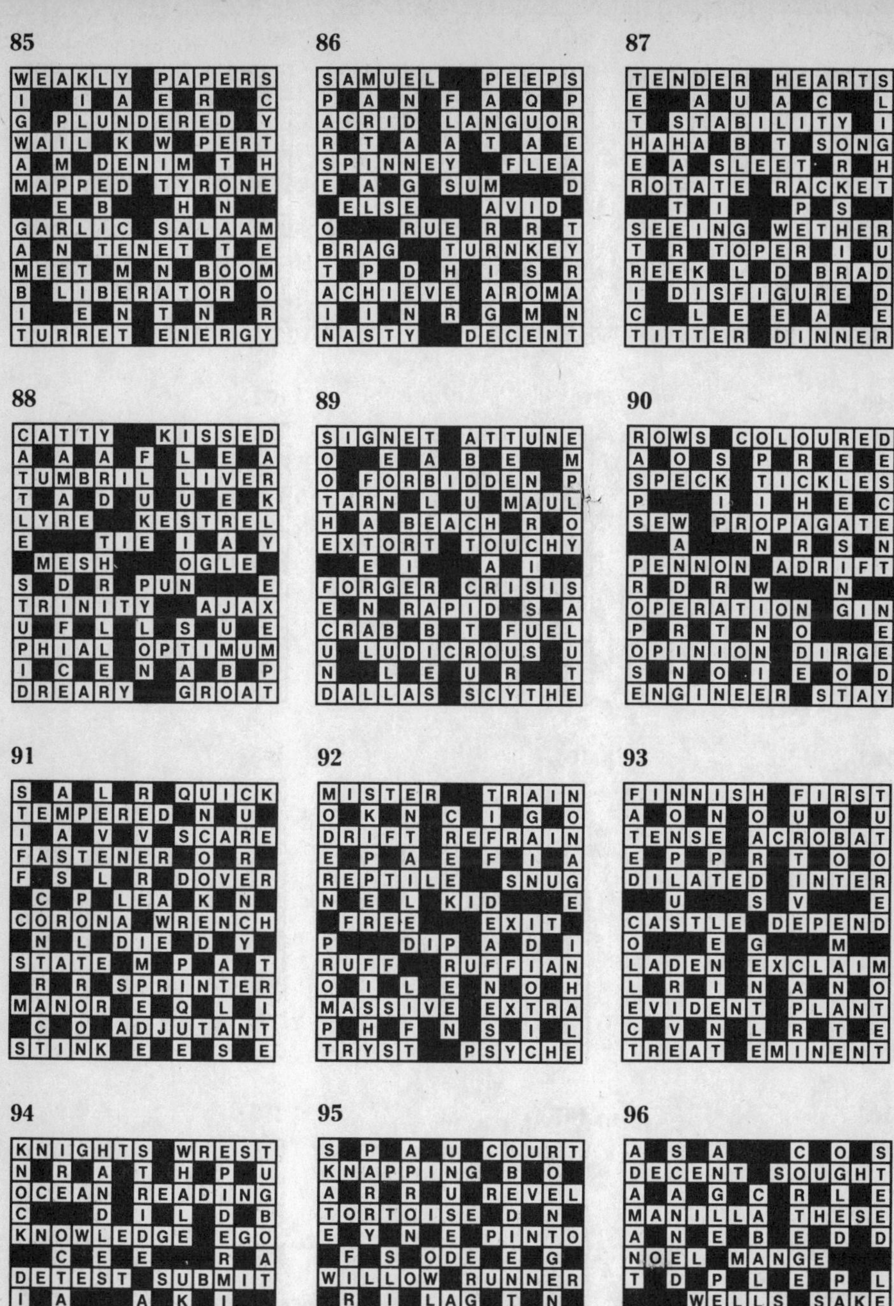

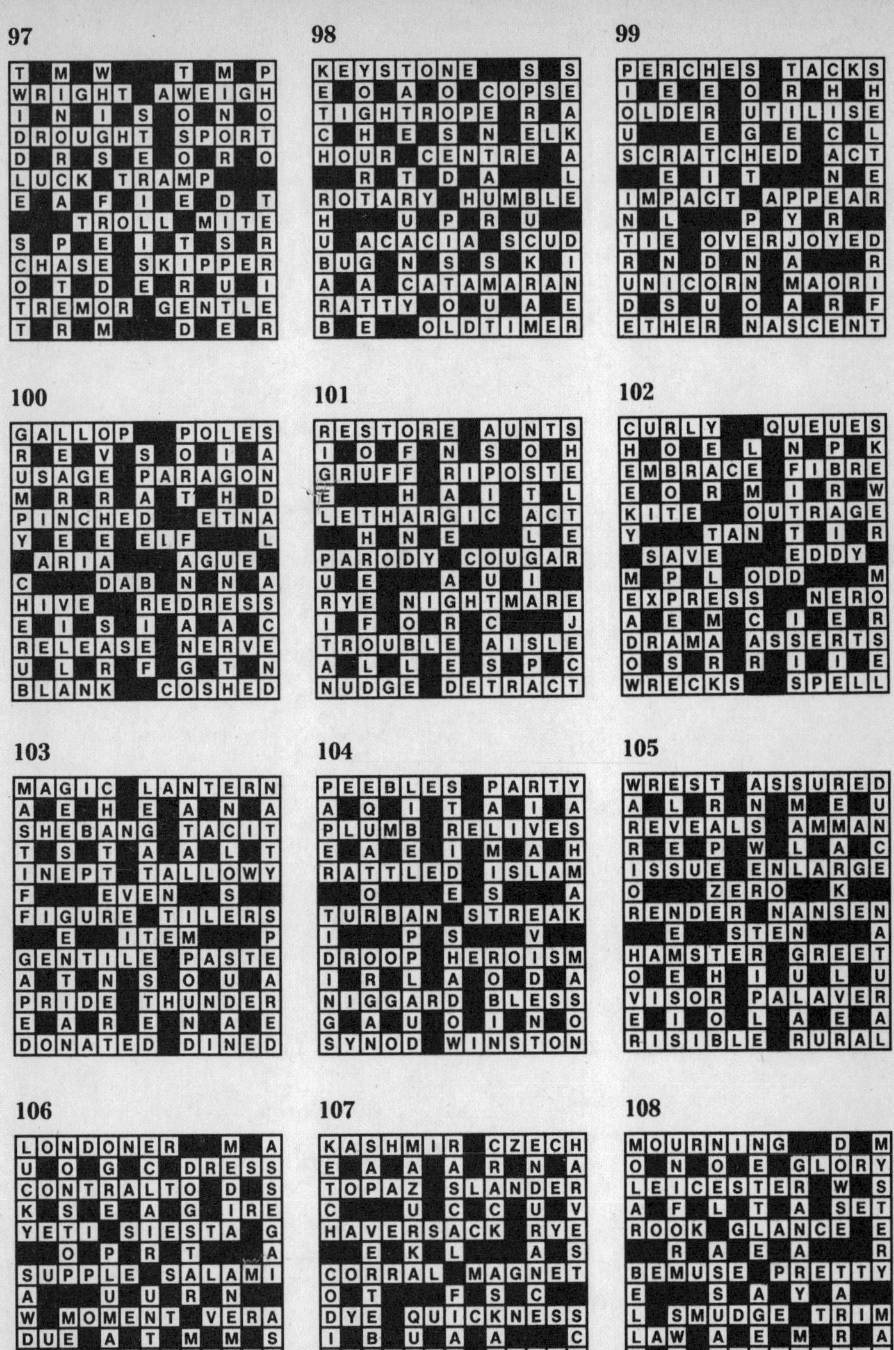
97
T M W T M P
WRIGHT AWEIGH
I N I S O N O
DROUGHT SPORT
D R S E O R O
LUCK TRAMP
E A F I E D T
TROLL MITE
S P E I T S R
CHASE SKIPPER
O T D E R U I
TREMOR GENTLE
T R M D E R
98
KEYSTONE S S
E O A O COPSE
TIGHTROPE R A
C H E S N ELK
HOUR CENTRE A
R T D A L
ROTARY HUMBLE
H U P R U
U ACACIA SCUD
BUG N S S K I
A A CATAMARAN
RATTY O U A E
B E OLDTIMER
99
PERCHES TACKS
I E E O R H H
OLDER UTILISE
U E G E C L
SCRATCHED ACT
E I T N E
IMPACT APPEAR
N L P Y R
TIE OVERJOYED
R N D N A R
UNICORN MAORI
D S U O A R F
ETHER NASCENT
100
GALLOP POLES
R E V S O I A
USAGE PARAGON
M R R A T H D
PINCHED ETNA
Y E E ELF L
ARIA AGUE
C DAB N N A
HIVE REDRESS
E I S I A A C
RELEASE NERVE
U L R F G T N
BLANK COSHED
101
RESTORE AUNTS
I O F N S O H
GRUFF RIPOSTE
E H A I T L
LETHARGIC ACT
H N E L E
PARODY COUGAR
U E A U I
RYE NIGHTMARE
I F O R C J
TROUBLE AISLE
A L L E S P C
NUDGE DETRACT
102
CURLY QUEUES
H O E L N P K
EMBRACE FIBRE
E O R M I R W
KITE OUTRAGE
Y TAN T I R
SAVE EDDY
M P L ODD M
EXPRESS NERO
A E M C I E R
DRAMA ASSERTS
O S R R I I E
WRECKS SPELL
103
MAGIC LANTERN
A E H E A N A
SHEBANG TACIT
T S T A A L T
INEPT TALLOWY
F EVEN S
FIGURE TILERS
E ITEM P
GENTILE PASTE
A T N S O U A
PRIDE THUNDER
E A R E N A E
DONATED DINED
104
PEEBLES PARTY
A Q I T A I A
PLUMB RELIVES
E A E I M A H
RATTLED ISLAM
O E S A
TURBAN STREAK
I P S V
DROOP HEROISM
I R L A O D A
NIGGARD BLESS
G A U O I N O
SYNOD WINSTON
105
WREST ASSURED
A L R N M E U
REVEALS AMMAN
R E P W L A C
ISSUE ENLARGE
O ZERO K
RENDER NANSEN
E STEN A
HAMSTER GREET
O E H I U L U
VISOR PALAVER
E I O L A E A
RISIBLE RURAL
106
LONDONER M A
U O G C DRESS
CONTRALTO D S
K S E A G IRE
YETI SIESTA G
O P R T A
SUPPLE SALAMI
A U U R N
W MOMENT VERA
DUE A T M M S
U R GARRULOUS
SPINE U L N E
T T VEHEMENT
107
KASHMIR CZECH
E A A A R N A
TOPAZ SLANDER
C U C C U V
HAVERSACK RYE
E K L A S
CORRAL MAGNET
O T F S C
DYE QUICKNESS
I B U A A C
CURTAIN NOISE
I A K C C R N
LIEGE ELEMENT
108
MOURNING D M
O N O E GLORY
LEICESTER W S
A F L T A SET
ROOK GLANCE E
R A E A R
BEMUSE PRETTY
E S A Y A
L SMUDGE TRIM
LAW A E M R A
O O GENTILITY
NURSE C M E O
A D CYLINDER

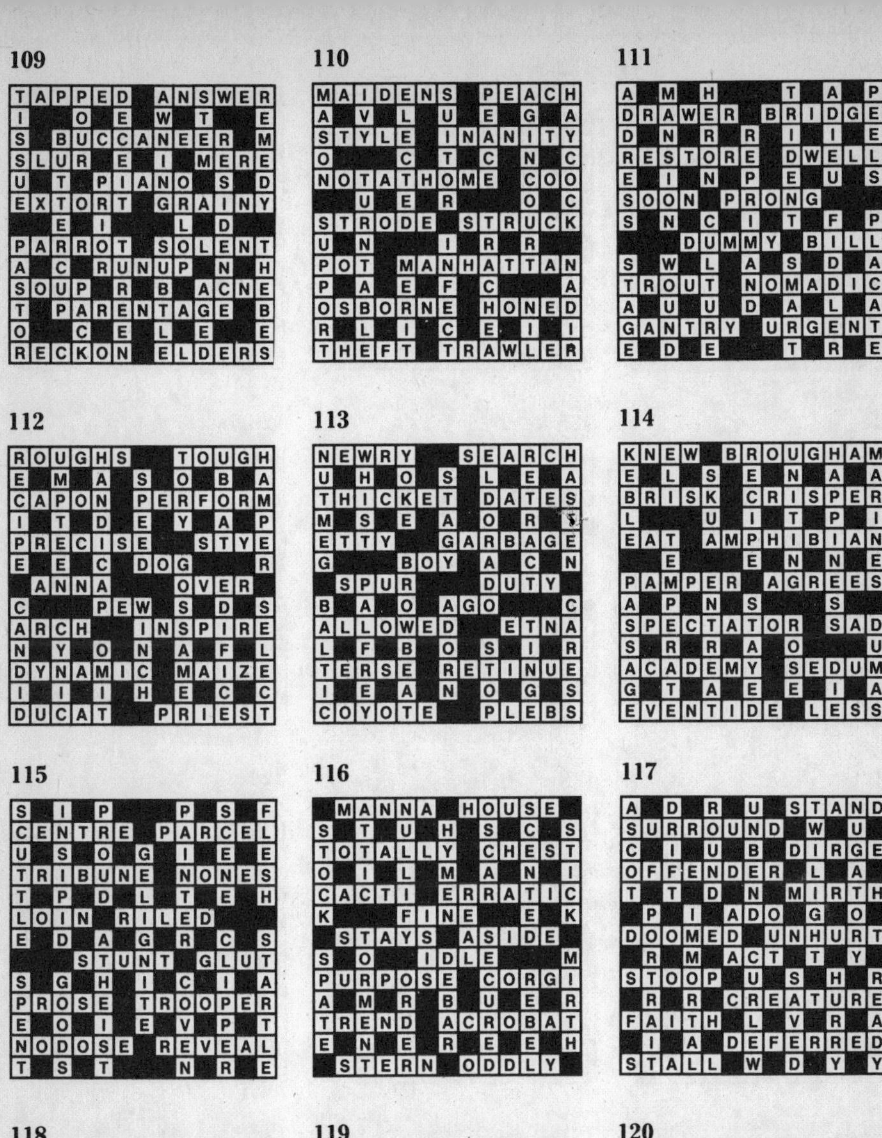

118

P	O	L	I	S	H	E	D			V		E
I		I		H		N		F	L	A	W	S
A	C	Q	U	I	E	S	C	E		L		S
N		U		P		I		L		U	R	E
O	B	E	Y		I	G	N	I	T	E		N
		U		D		N		N				C
C	A	R	P	E	T		P	E	B	B	L	E
O				N		R		S		U		
N		T	I	T	T	E	R		B	L	U	R
C	A	W		I		P		E		L		A
E		E		S	P	A	S	M	O	D	I	C
A	L	E	R	T		I		M		O		E
L		D			A	R	R	A	N	G	E	D

119

S		F		D				W		C		A
C	O	R	D	O	N		B	O	W	L	E	D
A		A		U		F		R		U		D
P	L	I	A	B	L	E		S	A	B	R	E
U		L		T		R		H		S		R
L	U	T	E		T	O	X	I	C			
A		Y		D		C		P		J		C
			L	U	P	I	N		L	A	V	A
S		A		R		O		P		M		M
T	O	S	C	A		U	N	A	W	A	R	E
O		T		B		S		R		I		L
C	H	I	L	L	Y		S	T	U	C	C	O
K		R		E				Y		A		T

120

C	R	E	W	E	L			S	E	I	Z	E
O		N		N		G		A		N		N
M	O	T	E	T		R	E	G	U	L	A	R
B		I		A		A		E		E		A
A	T	T	E	N	D	S			S	T	A	G
T		L		G		S	U	M				E
	P	E	E	L				U	R	G	E	
P				E	R	A		T		A		B
L	E	A	P			P	R	A	I	R	I	E
A		C		G		P		T		B		A
N	E	U	T	R	A	L		I	N	A	P	T
E		T		I		Y		O		G		E
T	R	E	A	D			U	N	S	E	E	N

121

HUNDRED WAITS
O U E E H N I
TONIC TRAVAIL
E E O L N E
LONGITUDE INN
O V R M C
MITTEN SAVAGE
E O W R T
TAR READINESS
H I U R Z T
AROUSED OZONE
N U T E N U E
ESSAY ROASTED

122

GRUESOME A E
R N P E ROSES
OBEDIENCE K P
O Q T A B EGO
MAUL ACCORD U
A D E U S
PALLID INVOKE
H V O D P
A SLEEVE SHAM
NUT R E A E A
T R GARIBALDI
ORATE D U I Z
M P BOOTLACE

123

QUIRE BUOYS
F N E U S A F
REMOVES ISSUE
I A E U N H I
LINEN REGIMEN
L GOYA A T
IMPEL ROCKY
L E ANNE B
ALEWIFE DELVE
N T M A I A A
CHINA REPORTS
E N G S U G T
AGREE ASPEN

124

HOBBY HOARSE
U O A A R E N
MINERAL NOVEL
B U D I A O I
EASY CUMULUS
R DYE E V T
MATE NEED
A M L SOT M
CRANIUM ABBE
T T C A E L N
OMEGA RESCIND
R U T T P N E
SCREEN YOKEL

125

B S B O B S
RUNOUT ESTEEM
A A L C S E I
MUFFLER ULCER
B F Y O A H K
LILT SWARD
E E P S Y B W
TRUNK FLEA
E N I E S O S
BREAM SPINACH
O I U T M T I
NIGGLE SOLEMN
Y H A N R G

126

CONSENT RATED
A E R A E R E
COWER SUCCESS
T S O T L N P
IMMERSE ULTRA
A D S I
BANNED KEEPER
A N V R
NOTED EXPLODE
Q H L R L P S
USELESS APHIS
E M S U T E E
TRESS SHORTEN

127

KARMA LIGHT
S P A D R E S
CARBINE ASSET
O I G F T S A
RULER OPENING
E EWER A E
CRATE OPINE
S A LODE F
CONSULT REPEL
R S T T P I E
EXACT ECLIPSE
E C E R E E T
SKIRT EXTRA

128

CAESAR CHANCE
A T O A G X
V BYSTANDER P
IBEX A C DOPE
A A CREEK C R
RUNWAY RACKET
F R P E
BREVET SORTIE
A A DRUNK I N
BASH U E SNAG
B TIMEBEING I
L D S R I N
EXPECT SUPPLE

129

MAILING LISZT
U C G E O P O
STERN WRITERS
I O G R C S
CELEBRATE TIP
I L W A O
TABLET FAUCET
Y E G N L
PAR PERTINENT
I A L I M I
COTTAGE ANNUL
A E C V T E E
LEDGE ERECTOR

130

AFFECTED B I
P L R L HEIRS
PROMENADE S O
L R W T A OWL
EXIT BERLIN A
S A D T T
INTEND CHOOSE
N A C Y M
V RETIRE SNAG
ERE O I A I R
R P MISERABLE
SALLY I E U E
E Y ASSASSIN

131

HACKS MINSTER
A O A U E O O
LINCTUS WOUND
I G C T E C I
BROTH EARTHEN
U EARL E
TRAILS SPADES
M THOR E
SCORPIO INDEX
T N I B N R T
ELGIN BOTTEGA
E S T L E A N
POTHOLE REMIT

132

SLEEPING I C
P L L E BIRTH
ELABORATE O A
E S T R N NIL
DATE ALTERS I
I C Y F C
NECTAR PIRATE
O P C T L
T ANIMAL TEAR
AWL T S O R I
B I ALIENATED
LEVEL N C E E
E E TOREADOR

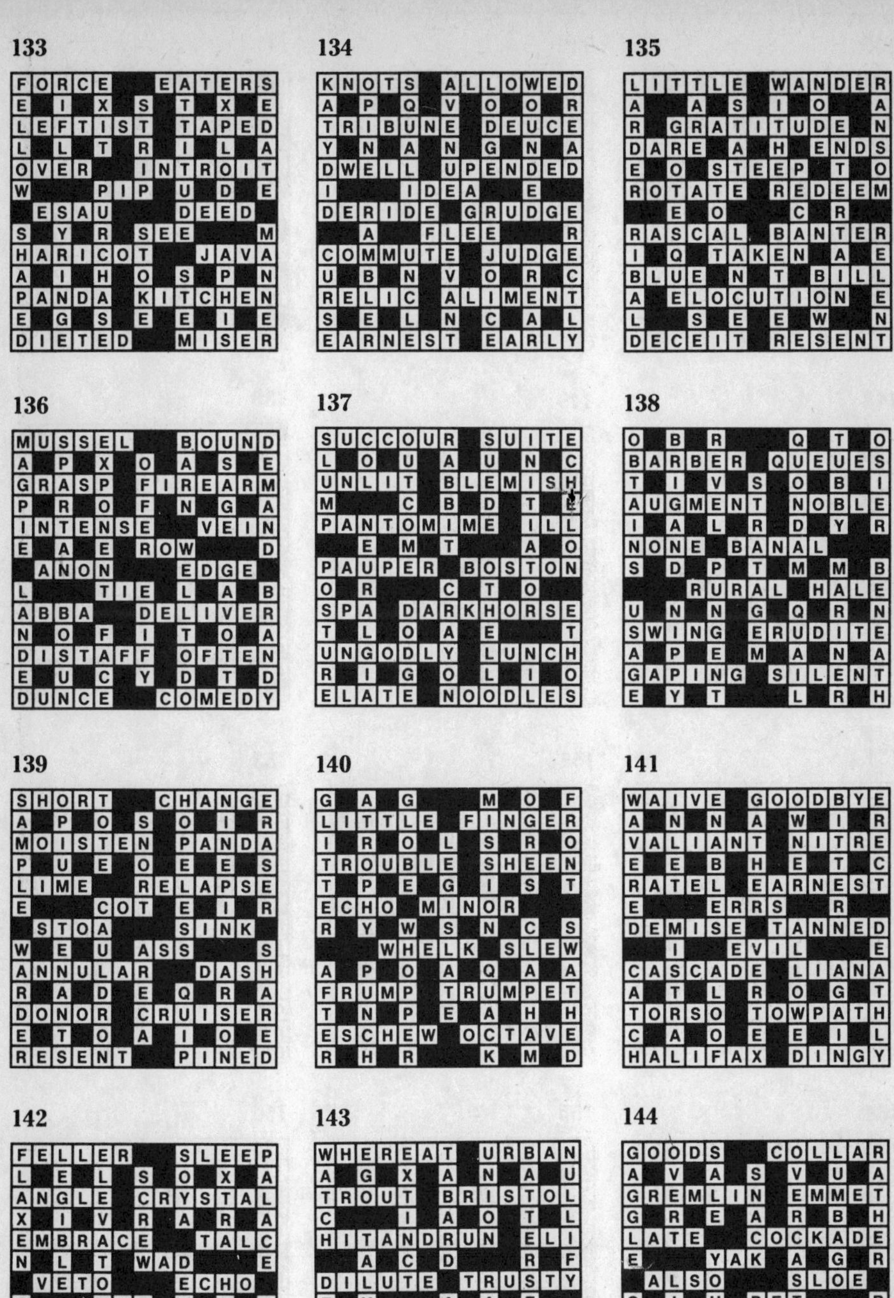

145

```
A S M   F S A
COPPER BOTTOM
T A R S O R P
UPRIGHT TRAIL
A T E E M W E
ROAM BANAL   
Y N S D N E P
   CHAFF AFAR
B R A A E F O
AMOUR SEGMENT
T M P T Y N E
CLEVER SPADES
H O N   T I T
```

146

```
WHACKS  WORKS
R U E S I H I
EAGLE ARRAIGN
A U N T E N N
TYRANNY  FETE
H E E RUB   R
 ODES   INCH 
P   SAP N H E
ROMP  LANTERN
I A P A A S Z
SOJOURN CATTY
O O S E L E M
NORTH  DECREE
```

147

```
O U M U BEECH
FASHIONS G A 
F H S T AGILE
ERECTION P A 
R R Y L BLAME
 H S ODD A I 
PASTOR ORNATE
 I U BAG T Y 
GREBE M R A O
 L B CALENDAR
DEMON Z B M D
 S R BENEFICE
USING D L T R
```

148

```
JEWEL CONTROL
U A I O O H I
PERFORM WHEAT
I E N E A N H
TASTE DAYTIME
E   STYX  S  
REFUSE LATHER
  A AGED    E
EXTREME ALARM
X I G N M S O
ANGER TEACHER
C U E L N E S
THEATRE TENSE
```

149

```
FORTY  CHEWED
I O A E O E R
BOOTLEG RODEO
U S E H N L V
LUTE  APPROVE
A   HAM I C R
 CAVY   PIKE 
S B A BYE   T
CORACLE  FAIR
R I I A P L A
AUDEN CHAMOIS
P G T H I F H
SEETHE  DITTY
```

150

```
 DINER MIGHT 
A N V A N A J
BULLIED AMPLE
E E D A N L T
LITHE PREVENT
E    NOTE S Y
 VESTA ABUSE 
A N  TALE   C
DELIGHT AUGER
A I O L R I E
GIVER AGITATE
E E S S N N L
 INTER AGATE 
```

151

```
WATCHER THINK
A A E E O N E
VITAL SERPENT
E T O I T P T
RELATED UNTIL
  E   E R   E
THROAT RECESS
A   L S   X  
NIGHT TWITTER
T A E R D R A
REMORSE LEAPT
U I E A E C E
MINED MERITED
```

152

```
C P M A CHILE
RESPONSE A E 
U A V S PRATE
MALDEMER A H 
B M D R OSCAR
 T B ETC S R 
BARREL AVENGE
 T I MAN D Y 
STEER L S S P
 E F OBSTACLE
GRAIN E A O T
 E N CRACKPOT
ADAGE T K E Y
```

153

```
SORE DAYLIGHT
P U G R U A E
EAGER ROSTRUM
E   I E T R P
DIM DESTITUTE
  A   T E L S
PASTEL TRYOUT
L T P B   U  
ELIMINATE SAW
D C C I D   H
GRADUAL GNOME
E T R I E D L
DEEPENED WEAK
```

154

```
M O R   P O A
AFFAIR GROUND
S F F F O T O
SCHOLAR CIDER
I A E O E O E
VANE OSIER   
E D B T D H I
   GLOBE DAWN
E A O I M B K
BOGUS TRIVIAL
O A S E S T I
NOTION REMAIN
Y E M   R T G
```

155

```
DIVE URGENTLY
A O A E M R A
TOWEL PRIMERS
E   P E N M H
SET STATEROOM
  E   T N L A
PATOIS ATTACK
E E C B   N  
GRAVESEND TIP
A T P A U   E
STEWING TRAIN
U T C L Y I N
SPECKLED EDDY
```

156

```
COMPERE NOTES
L I A X U H E
ELGAR PUNGENT
A R T O N F T
REACHES EXTOL
  T   E R   E
FLEECE BYWORD
A   O A   P  
SAFER STOPPER
H A I L C R A
INCENSE CHEAP
O E T E U S I
NOTCH PERUSED
```

157

SHARP TURNING
T R R H I N U
EXECUTE GAVEL
R N D M H I E
IRATE ESTATES
L NASH E
EIGHTS ASIDES
A IOWA U
PERSIAN COLIC
O B S W K A C
WALES AMIABLE
E E U R N E S
REDHEAD GALES

158

DRIVING REIGN
I L N A A M E
VALID RELAPSE
E O N L R D
DISCOVERY OIL
O R T M E
POLISH RUMPUS
E I C N T
RUT MULTITUDE
H A E E F E
AVIATOR OFFER
P R R I R E I
SWEDE COMPETE

159

ALMOND PACED
R E E S L H E
MANIA PROSAIC
A T R A T R E
DEIGNED OMEN
A O E END T
ONUS IDOL
S SAD S P C
ARCH ANGUISH
C O S N R N O
RELATED AMISS
E O I Y C O E
DINAR PENNON

160

DRESSING A R
O R K O TABLE
PRETENDER U P
E C W U A SOL
DATE ELAPSE A
E L E P C
CADGER HEARSE
A C P R O
P SUTURE STOW
TIP E E H A A
I A RESPECTED
ONION T A E E
N N COMPOSED

161

T S P S GUARD
HENPARTY N E
U O S U EGYPT
MARITIME U T
P E A E FLAIR
M S ORB A L
WALESA ENTAIL
L D KIT E A
LIVID N A B S
N T OFFSHORE
AGAIN A I G V
E O IMMATURE
WRONG Y N S R

162

HABITUAL T A
O A R K LYRES
MARGARINE A S
E R Y M V IRE
RAID ABSENT R
E A O R T
PARODY TENNIS
A D A T O
S STUMPS STEM
SUM C P H I
A E EXECUTION
GLAND A M N E
E R ARRANGED

163

SKIRT INBOARD
C N O G A N R
ANDIRON NOISE
L U M I T L A
POSSE TOURISM
E NEED N
LAPUTA EFFECT
I SARI A
MINARET SATIN
U T I H H U K
SWARD ENNOBLE
I I G N E E R
CALLERS TORTS

164

PIQUANT SHOES
O U S I A R P
SKIMP CITADEL
E B I K C E A
DEBACLE HURRY
L T E E
PRECIS ELUDED
R N S R
OVERT TOPSIDE
J M E R U L E
EXPUNGE RULER
C T S E G E I
THYME TREADLE

165

AFFIXED STAIR
L I I O L U E
ALBUM CRUISER
R E T S T E
MACINTOSH ROD
A E R A O
FOREST SCALES
E P I A I
SUE LEGISLATE
T N A N S A
ONTARIO OPENS
O E G R C L E
NERVE ESKIMOS

166

CARRIER TORCH
L E N E O E O
APPLE CERTAIN
S T P E N D E
STILTON ABYSS
L T D T
GREECE DONKEY
E A E N
NATAL FORMULA
E R Y F U C R
SCORPIO POKER
I U S R E L A
SETTO THEREIN

167

START EARNS
S W O B L O W
PIANOLA PUNCH
U N S L H P I
MIGHT STAPLES
E ESAU U T
SHORT BOAST
W A OPAL S
AGRIPPA YOKEL
L B A U M Y O
THORN SUPPORT
Z U D E I T H
BROAD MANOR

168

TOFFEE KNOWS
E U L P I U A
LUCID ANTONYM
L H O N E C P
ENSURED KEEL
R I A ART E
BALD RAGE
R ORB A L P
EASE REPLICA
P A S E P D D
EXPIATE ILIAD
A I G D S N E
LADLE STAGED

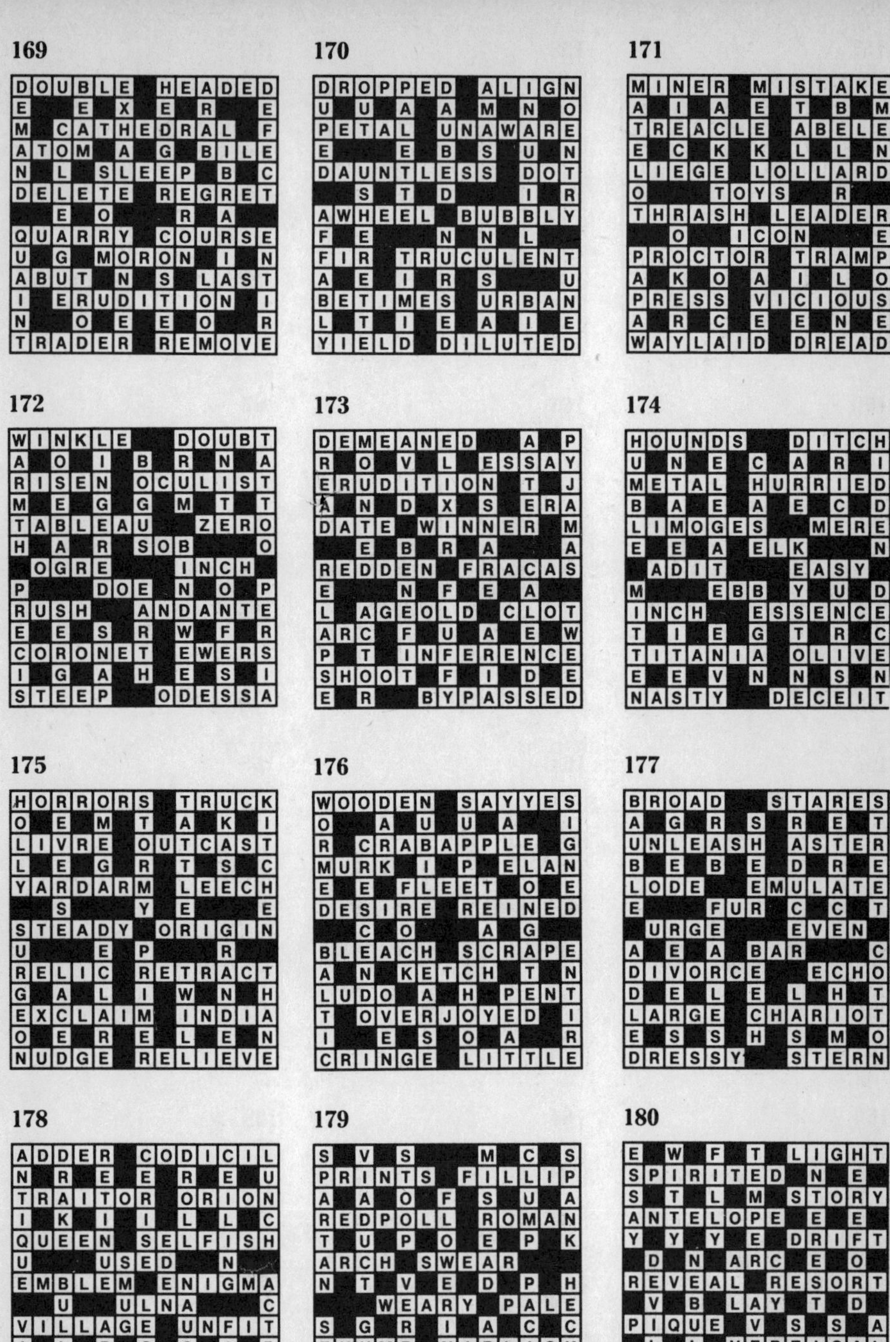
169
170
171
172
173
174
175
176
177
178
179
180

181

P	E	N	N	Y		B	I	Z	A	R	R	E
A		I		I		O		E		E		N
P	I	G	M	E	N	T		B	R	A	N	D
Y		H		L		T		R		C		E
R	A	T	E	D		L	O	A	T	H	E	D
U				E	V	E	N			E		
S	T	R	O	D	E		C	R	A	D	L	E
		E			T	R	E	E				N
S	H	A	M	P	O	O		F	R	I	E	D
T		L		I		T		L		R		L
E	L	I	Z	A		A	V	E	R	A	G	E
A		T		N		T		C		T		S
K	E	Y	H	O	L	E		T	R	E	S	S

182

A	N	C	H	O	R		W	R	I	T	E	S
R			U		A		A		R			T
C		P	R	I	N	C	I	P	A	L		A
H	O	O	T		C		V		N	O	O	N
E		S		C	I	V	E	T		N		C
R	O	T	T	E	D		D	I	N	G	L	E
		I		D				L		E		
P	I	L	L	A	R		P	L	O	V	E	R
U		I		R	O	L	L	S		I		E
Z	O	O	M		T		E		S	T	E	M
Z		N	A	T	U	R	A	L	L	Y		I
L			G		N		S		I			S
E	N	V	I	E	D		E	X	P	E	L	S

183

A		P		S		S		A	D	D	E	R
G	O	O	D	T	I	M	E		I		N	
O		P		R		I		P	S	A	L	M
N	U	P	T	I	A	L	S		P		A	
Y		Y		P		E		T	A	R	R	Y
	H		C		O	D	D		T		G	
C	A	L	L	O	W		E	X	C	E	E	D
	N		A		L	O	W		H		D	
A	D	O	R	N		P		R		S		B
	I		E		R	A	D	I	A	T	O	R
S	C	A	N	T		Q		F		A		I
	A		C		P	U	B	L	I	C	A	N
S	P	R	E	E		E		E		K		K

184

B	O	S	U	N		N	A	R	R	O	W	S
I		O		U		I		E		U		H
C	A	B	A	R	E	T		V	O	T	E	R
Y		E		T		W		U		R		E
C	O	R	F	U		I	C	E	L	A	N	D
L				R	I	T	E			G		
E	X	C	E	E	D		D	I	V	E	R	S
		O			E	V	E	N				Y
M	A	T	I	S	S	E		N	I	C	E	R
U		T		W		N		I		L		I
M	I	A	M	I		D	U	N	G	E	O	N
P		G		F		O		G		A		G
S	H	E	L	T	E	R		S	I	N	G	E

185

O		B		V				G		S		I
S	T	O	R	E	Y		T	E	L	L	E	R
T		U		N		S		N		E		A
R	E	L	E	A	S	E		E	V	E	N	T
I		D		L		L		R		K		E
C	H	E	F		L	E	G	A	L			
H		R		M		C		L		G		D
			P	A	R	T	Y		C	A	R	E
K		A		R		I		A		M		N
N	I	G	E	R		O	M	N	I	B	U	S
A		I		I		N		N		L		I
V	A	L	U	E	D		M	O	D	E	S	T
E		E		D				Y		D		Y

186

F	O	U	N	D	E	R		P	L	A	C	E
A		R		E		E		L		L		C
K	I	N	G	S		C	H	A	T	T	E	L
I				S		E		I		I		I
R	E	P	R	E	S	S	E	D		M	A	P
		A		R		S				E		S
P	O	T	A	T	O		M	E	T	T	L	E
I		E				R		N		E		
G	A	R		T	H	E	S	A	U	R	U	S
T		N		I		C		C				E
A	M	I	A	B	L	E		T	H	O	R	N
I		T		E		N		E		W		O
L	A	Y	E	R		T	I	D	D	L	E	R

187

V	I	S	I	T	I	N	G			E		D
I		A		U		O		T	H	Y	M	E
O	P	P	O	R	T	U	N	E		R		V
L		L		F		G		D		I	R	E
A	R	I	D		C	H	O	I	C	E		L
		N		P		T		O				O
A	U	G	U	R	Y		T	U	R	N	I	P
V				O		F		S		A		
E		D	E	B	R	I	S		C	R	A	B
R	Y	E		L		A		A		R		U
A		C		E	A	S	Y	C	H	A	I	R
G	R	O	O	M		C		R		T		S
E		Y			C	O	H	E	R	E	N	T

188

S	A	W	Y	E	R			B	E	A	N	S
P		H		C		F		E		W		P
R	H	I	N	O		L	U	G	G	A	G	E
U		T		N		U		S		R		E
C	U	T	S	O	F	F			B	E	N	D
E		L		M		F	A	G				Y
	Y	E	T	I				R	I	T	E	
M				C	U	P		A		U		D
E	A	S	Y			I	N	F	E	R	N	O
R		C		P		E		F		N		R
L	O	O	K	O	U	T		I	R	O	N	S
I		L		S		Y		T		U		A
N	O	D	D	Y			P	I	S	T	O	L

189

H	E	A	R	T			L	E	S	L	I	E
A		M		R		A		X		U		L
Z	E	A	L	O	U	S		T	U	L	L	E
A		S		Y		I		E		L		C
R	U	S	E			D	O	R	M	A	N	T
D				B	E	E		I		B		S
	O	V	E	R				O	N	Y	X	
E		A		U		S	I	R				B
S	Y	N	O	N	Y	M			S	O	U	R
T		I		E		A		A		I		E
A	L	L	O	T		R	E	V	O	L	V	E
T		L		T		T		O		E		Z
E	N	A	M	E	L			N	U	D	G	E

190

E		S		T				P		O		E
J	A	C	K	I	N		T	H	E	B	O	X
E		A		B		S		A		E		U
C	O	N	S	E	N	T		N	A	S	A	L
T		D		R		A		T		E		T
E	D	A	M		E	L	B	O	W			
D		L		T		E		M		S		E
			C	R	A	M	P		S	H	U	T
U		H		U		A		R		A		E
S	W	A	R	M		T	R	A	W	L	E	R
A		S		P		E		V		L		N
G	A	T	H	E	R		P	E	L	O	T	A
E		Y		T				L		T		L

191

G	R	A	C	E		D	A	R	L	I	N	G
A		M		J		I		A		N		I
R	E	P	R	E	S	S		C	E	D	E	D
L		L		C		C		E		I		D
A	V	E	R	T		U	N	R	E	A	D	Y
N				E	A	S	E			N		
D	E	L	U	D	E		W	A	R	S	A	W
		A			O	A	T	S				A
C	U	R	R	A	N	T		P	O	S	E	R
A		G		P		T		H		T		A
S	H	E	B	A		A	N	A	L	Y	S	T
E		S		C		I		L		L		A
D	I	S	C	E	R	N		T	E	E	T	H

192

T		I		A				E		A		W
R	E	S	I	S	T		S	T	A	N	C	E
I		O		S		A		E		G		L
B	A	L	L	A	S	T		R	U	R	A	L
U		A		Y		H		N		Y		S
T	U	T	U		C	L	E	A	R			
E		E		M		E		L		P		T
			F	A	I	T	H		B	E	E	R
T		E		D		I		E		R		O
H	A	L	V	E		C	A	R	E	F	U	L
E		E		I		S		U		E		L
F	I	G	U	R	E		A	P	A	C	H	E
T		Y		A				T		T		Y

193

```
SWITCH COARSE
L A A O V U
I STANCHION C
CITE D O NOEL
E I FLIRT C I
DEMURE TASTED
U O T U
ALLOTS STEREO
F A HASTY N V
FATE L A PACE
E EDITORIAL R
C I E V C D
TUFTED ESKIMO
```

194

```
G S U D GRATE
UNWASHED E E
S A U V STARE
TOMORROW U M
O P P U GRAIN
H P ARM N N
CYPRUS AVENUE
S I HAY D S
STUMP M S F O
E R BANKRUPT
PROOF Z A N T
I S CONTINUE
HAVEN N E Y R
```

195

```
PLAYBILL C O
A L O E YARDS
CABALLERO A T
T E T W G GAR
SPRY PATHOS I
T V Y U C
CHALET WRAITH
A S G T M
M SETTLE WARY
EAT I A M G A
L A GONDOLIER
OLIVE C O N N
T D FEARLESS
```

196

```
BANNED MASTER
A E R O E O
T PARAMOUNT L
TIER P R DEAL
E C DETER R E
ROUSES DEARER
N M G I
SAILOR BANTER
U A NAVAL O E
DART F R BRAD
D YESTERDAY D
E S E I S E
NECTAR ENSIGN
```

197

```
WEARING AVAIL
A C N L G P I
THEME APROPOS
C R N E R T
HEARTACHE ELI
L I E H N
PILLAR BADEGG
A I C L N
PIG BARTENDER
Y A O O R O
RETRACT TIBIA
U O R C E O S
SHRED HYDRANT
```

198

```
LITTLE KNELL
O I U I I A A
VALID MANAGER
E L D A D E I
LEAVING AREA
Y G T END T
FETE READ
D SAP U M A
RASH REDHEAD
A W S A G R H
GOURMET ELITE
O N U E R C R
NIGHT GYRATE
```

199

```
CREWS MISSILE
A V H A P N Y
PROLONG USHER
I K R P R A I
TRENT IGNOBLE
A EDEN I
LITANY AUNTIE
O EATS M
INDOORS EQUIP
N D F H L N R
DELFT OVERDUE
I E E R S E S
ARRANGE SORTS
```

200

```
HANSOM FELLER
A K I I I E
M SIGNALLER G
POET G L DEER
E N FLEET M E
RETIRE TRUANT
I A U I
MOMENT SCONCE
O E KAYAK D X
LINT L M JEEP
E TRIMESTER O
S O U O H R
TESTED NOUGHT
```

201

```
HARPY MEDIUM
U O E S N N A
MAUDLIN VOCAL
B N L O I L L
LODE OBSCURE
E FOP A D T
AJAR GREY
O E A SUE C
DRAUGHT SPUR
E L M O W U A
SHORE LEAFLET
S U N E N S E
ASSETS DREAR
```

202

```
BRED PUDDINGS
A L S N I A A
ROMEO REACTOR
G L E L U A
ELL OBSTETRIC
I T C A E
PAMPAS STOLEN
A O D T L
LAUNDRESS YES
M S R N I T
ICINESS LAVER
S N S O T A U
TREASURE STEM
```

203

```
A C L P P A
BROKER RECORD
S U V S R L D
CONVERT FLAKE
O S L E U R R
NEED BALMY
D L S D E C A
QUAFF CLAD
A B N A F O D
BROOD STUMBLE
Y G O T N B N
SQUAWK INTEND
S S N Y R A
```

204

```
CLOSE BASKETS
A L R R E N I
PRIVATE PAVED
I V S E I I E
THERM ZEALOUS
A USED U
LOCUST GLASSY
L AREA A
PREPARE MOSES
L M T C B H H
AVERT OVERARM
T N I R N K A
ENTICED TWEAK
```

205

```
S#S#L#S#PANEL
PATIENCE#C#X#
A#A#T#O#SCOPE
TOMAHAWK#U#O#
E#P#E#L#BRUSH
#O#F#ASH#A#U#
ABSURD#OUTCRY
#L#N#DIP#E#E#
FINCH#N#P#P#S
#V#T#ACCIDENT
VIVID#O#L#R#E
#O#O#EMPORIUM
INANE#E#T#L#S
```

206

```
SKATER##ROUND
U#S#V#G#I#T#O
PRIME#ROTATED
P#N#N#A#E#E#G
EVICTED##BRIE
R#N#U#EAT###D
#HERA###HIDE#
P###LOT#E#E#O
RUSH##ROOSTER
O#H#C#A#C#R#C
PEOPLED#REACH
E#R#A#E#A#C#I
RATED##STATED
```

207

```
MEATIER#RIGHT
A#C#S#E#E#A#E
FERAL#FEMALES
I#O#E#O#I#E#T
ARBITER#NISEI
##A###M#D###F
MOTHER#ESTRAY
E###M#C###E##
SAHIB#LINEAGE
S#O#A#I#U#L#L
INTERNE#BLIND
A#E#G#N#I#S#E
HELLO#TRAITOR
```

208

```
CHECKER#BORED
R#L#I#E#I#E#U
UNION#NEBULAR
M###G#O#L#U#A
BROADSIDE#COB
##F#O#R###T#L
INFAMY#SQUARE
N#S###C#U#N##
SOP#BARRISTER
I#R#A#A#N###U
GAINSAY#IXION
H#N#I#O#N#L#E
TIGON#NEEDLES
```

209

```
A#P#A#I#UNDER
STANDING#E#X#
T#N#U#S#AGATE
INSULATE#A#E#
R#Y#T#E#STONE
#P#A#APE#I#D#
BETTER#REVIEW
#R#T#TOR#E#D#
ASHEN#I#L#B#S
#O#M#PLEASURE
SNIPE#I#B#D#E
#A#T#INTENDED
GLASS#G#L#Y#Y
```

210

```
GENERALS##T#S
A#E#A#I#TAWSE
TRUMPETER#I#T
E#T#T#T#I#NET
DARE#PEBBLE#L
##A#L#R#U###E
MILLET#STATER
O###C#P#E#A##
C#SUTURE#OMIT
KIT#E#I#F#B#I
E#R#RESERVOIR
REIGN#O#E#U#E
Y#P##INTERRED
```

211

```
PLAYS##ATTUNE
I#M#A#P#H#N#R
NEEDFUL#EIDER
N#N#E#E#S#E#A
EDDY##ASPIRIN
D###ODD#I#G#D
#SNUB###AGOG#
H#U#D#WAN###S
EXCLUDE##SHUT
R#L#R#I#E#A#A
ARENA#RUSTLER
L#U#T#D#P#V#E
DISPEL##YIELD
```

212

```
T#S#S#S#WRITE
APPROACH#O#R#
L#A#L#O#TOTAL
EXCAVATE#S#I#
S#E#E#C#STALE
#M#D#SHE#E#I#
PANAMA#AIRING
#N#L#PAR#S#G#
ATOMS#N#L#L#L
#I#A#ENVELOPE
SLATE#U#P#V#N
#L#I#BASEMENT
LANCE#L#R#R#O
```

213

```
HARASSED##D#A
O#E#I#N#WEEDS
VIGILANCE#L#U
E#A#K#E#D#TAN
LOTH#DAHLIA#D
##T#I#D#O###E
QUAINT#ECLAIR
U###F#F#K#V##
A#STAIRS#HOST
RIP#N#A#L#C#H
R#E#CONNEMARA
ENEMY#C#A#D#N
L#D##YEARBOOK
```

214

```
A#A#F###A#S#S
CASTES#ADRIFT
C#S#L#A#V#N#E
OMINOUS#ANGLE
U#S#N#S#N#E#D
NOTE#WITCH###
T#S#A#D#E#A#A
###STOUT#OMEN
T#A#T#O#M#N#I
WATER#USELESS
I#L#A#S#R#S#E
STANCE#WRITHE
T#S#T###Y#Y#D
```

215

```
SETTER##LIMIT
O#O#Y#M#O#O#I
LAPSE#AMOROUS
A#M#S#N#M#S#S
CLOSING##MENU
E#S#G#END###E
#ITCH###ORTS#
C###TOO#M#R#C
HOCK##FLEMISH
O#A#M#T#S#B#E
RESPITE#TRUCE
U#E#N#N#I#T#S
SADAT##ACCEDE
```

216

```
TUMBLED#DOVER
A#U#O#E#O#O#E
MUMPS#STUDIED
E#M#E#E#B#C#H
DRESSER#THEME
##R###T#E###A
MAYHEM#ADORED
A###N#S###E##
GRANT#WARBLER
N#Z#R#A#I#A#E
ACUTELY#NEPAL
T#R#A#E#S#S#I
ERECT#DEEPEST
```

217

A		C		B		E		H	A	V	E	N
P	R	O	G	R	E	S	S		R		L	
P		M		A		C		A	S	S	E	T
A	R	M	E	N	I	A	N		O		V	
L		A		D		P		A	N	Z	A	C
	D		E		L	E	E		I		T	
L	E	S	S	E	E		V	I	S	I	O	N
	S		C		A	G	E		T		R	
D	E	L	A	Y		A		T		B		E
	R		P		A	L	S	A	T	I	A	N
S	T	R	A	P		L		C		G		E
	E		D		B	O	O	K	W	O	R	M
A	R	M	E	D		N		Y		T		Y

218

J	E	W	E	L		P	U	R	P	O	S	E
U		E		U		I		O		R		N
P	R	I	N	C	E	S		G	U	I	L	T
I		R		E		T		U		F		R
T	U	D	O	R		O	B	E	S	I	T	Y
E				N	I	L	E			C		
R	A	C	K	E	T		E	F	F	E	C	T
		O			C	U	R	E				O
U	P	R	I	G	H	T		R	E	C	U	R
R		S		R		O		V		H		P
G	R	A	P	E		P	R	E	P	A	R	E
E		I		E		I		N		R		D
S	Y	R	I	N	G	A		T	E	M	P	O

219

B	O	S	U	N			E	R	R	O	R	S
A		E		I		E		E		P		T
N	O	N	A	G	O	N		F	R	I	A	R
G		D		H		E		U		N		I
L	A	S	T			M	A	N	K	I	N	D
E				S	H	Y		D		O		E
	F	I	F	E				E	T	N	A	
B		N		N		B	I	D				R
E	L	E	C	T	O	R			B	A	S	E
A		X		I		A		H		P		V
C	H	A	I	N		C	L	I	M	A	T	E
O		C		E		E		D		R		A
N	E	T	T	L	E			E	X	T	O	L

220 **221** **222**

223 **224** **225**

226 **227** **228**

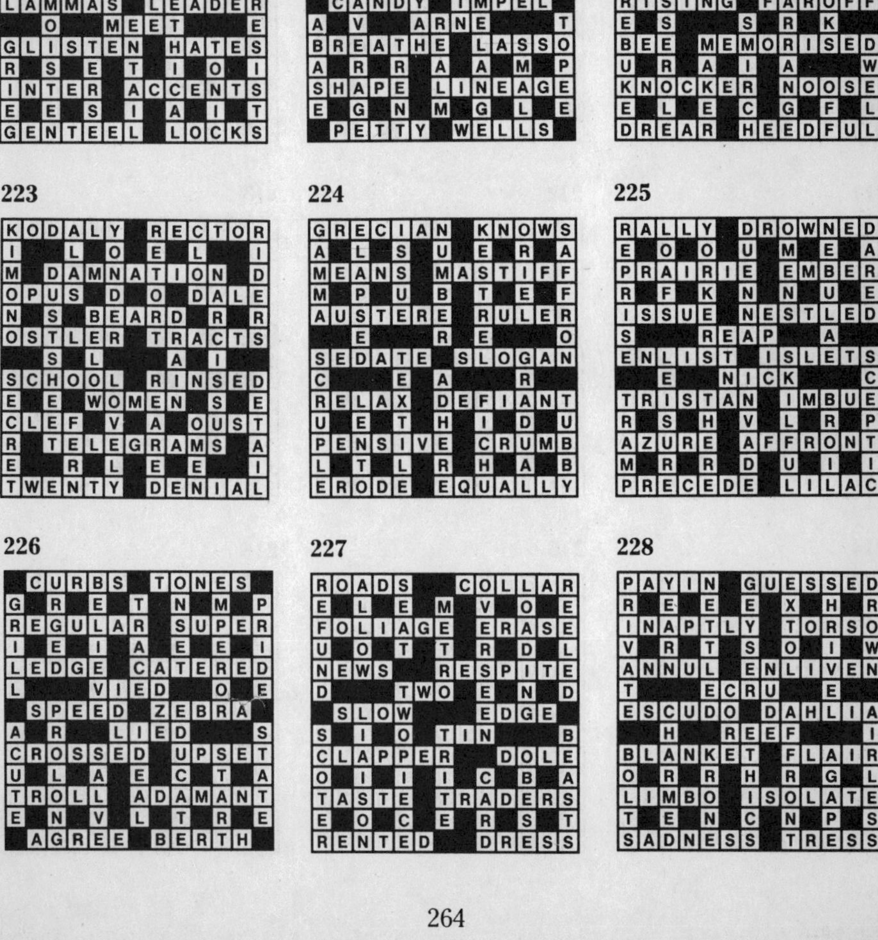

229

D	U	E	L		C	O	N	T	R	O	L	S
I		B		B		P		E		D		E
T	A	B	L	E		P	A	R	A	D	E	D
C				L		O		R		F		A
H	O	D		T	E	S	T	A	M	E	N	T
		E				E		C		L		E
B	E	L	O	N	G		Y	E	L	L	E	D
U		I		I		H				O		
R	E	C	O	G	N	I	S	E		W	E	T
G		I		G		D		M				H
L	E	O	P	A	R	D		M	A	K	E	R
A		U		R		E		A		I		O
R	E	S	I	D	E	N	T		K	N	O	B

230

H	I	G	H	E	R			D	O	U	B	T
U		L		X		P		O		S		O
R	O	A	S	T		L	A	N	G	U	I	D
D		N		E		U		E		R		D
L	A	C	O	N	I	C			O	P	A	L
E		E		D		K	I	D				E
	I	D	L	E				A	R	M	Y	
T				D	O	G		U		A		C
O	A	K	S			R	E	G	A	T	T	A
S		N		S		E		H		I		J
S	P	A	R	K	L	E		T	A	N	G	O
U		V		Y		T		E		E		L
P	I	E	C	E			B	R	E	E	Z	E

231

S		E		B		I		W	E	A	R	Y
C	O	V	E	R	I	N	G		D		E	
O		E		A		S		G	U	S	T	O
R	E	N	O	V	A	T	E		C		O	
E		T		E		E		H	A	I	R	Y
	T		A		A	P	E		T		T	
W	I	N	D	O	W		A	T	O	N	E	D
	R		H		E	R	R		R		D	
R	E	V	E	L		U		T		P		B
	S		R		J	E	W	E	L	L	E	R
T	O	N	I	C		F		E		E		U
	M		N		S	U	B	T	R	A	C	T
B	E	I	G	E		L		H		D		E

232

L	I	T	T	E	R			A	L	L	E	Y
E		R		L		R		R		I		O
T	R	I	T	E		U	N	C	L	E	A	N
T		P		G		L		H		G		D
E	X	P	I	A	T	E			M	E	R	E
R		E		N		R	I	P				R
	E	R	I	C				R	I	F	E	
P				E	G	G		E		U		A
R	A	S	H			R	E	V	E	R	E	D
I		H		M		A		I		T		V
E	M	O	T	I	O	N		O	L	I	V	E
S		C		E		D		U		V		N
T	O	K	E	N			A	S	P	E	C	T

233

	P	I	E	C	E		M	A	K	E	R	
M		C		O		V		D		N		T
A	M	I	A	B	L	E		O	C	C	U	R
D		N		B		S		R		L		E
A	N	G	L	E		P	A	N	C	A	K	E
M				R	O	A	D			V		S
	M	E	N	S	A		A	G	R	E	E	
R		X			S	E	M	I				C
E	X	P	E	R	T	S		B	E	L	L	E
L		R		A		S		L		O		L
A	V	E	R	T		A	S	E	X	U	A	L
X		S		E		Y		T		S		O
	A	S	I	D	E		U	S	H	E	R	

234

P	E	D	I	G	R	E	E			T		A
O		E		L		N		C	O	W	E	S
A	G	G	R	E	G	A	T	E		I		P
C		R		N		M		L		S	U	E
H	E	A	P		Z	E	A	L	O	T		R
		D		D		L		I				S
C	H	E	R	R	Y		A	S	H	O	R	E
R				E		Z		T		P		
A		S	I	S	K	I	N		P	U	N	T
C	O	W		S		R		B		L		O
K		E		E	X	C	E	L	L	E	N	T
U	N	D	E	R		O		U		N		E
P		E			I	N	D	E	B	T	E	D

235

F	I	G	H	T	E	R		P	L	A	I	N
L		L		O		E		I		G		O
U	N	I	O	N		M	E	M	E	N	T	O
K		T		I		E		E		E		D
E	N	T	I	C	E	D		N	A	S	A	L
		E				Y		T				E
B	A	R	G	E	E		C	O	U	N	T	S
A				X		S				O		
C	O	B	R	A		O	P	E	N	I	N	G
K		A		M		R		X		S		U
I	N	S	I	P	I	D		A	L	O	N	E
N		I		L		I		C		M		S
G	E	N	R	E		D	I	T	H	E	R	S

236

B		E		S				I		E		I
A	C	T	I	N	G		U	N	I	S	O	N
N		H		A		P		F		S		D
Q	U	I	N	I	N	E		A	D	A	G	E
U		C		L		N		N		Y		X
E	X	A	M		S	T	O	C	K			
T		L		L		H		Y		S		P
			V	E	N	O	M		S	T	A	R
S		H		A		U		M		I		O
T	R	O	U	T		S	H	A	L	L	O	T
A		B		H		E		C		T		E
G	O	B	L	E	T		F	A	M	O	U	S
E		Y		R				W		N		T

237

W		U		R		A		G	U	A	R	D
H	E	N	P	A	R	T	Y		M		O	
I		I		L		T		O	B	E	S	E
P	R	O	C	L	A	I	M		R		E	
S		N		Y		R		D	E	R	M	A
	M		P		T	E	A		L		A	
W	A	L	L	O	W		C	E	L	E	R	Y
	L		U		O	U	T		A		Y	
M	A	L	M	O		R		S		S		O
	P		B		E	G	G	T	I	M	E	R
P	E	D	A	L		E		R		A		I
	R		G		I	N	T	A	G	L	I	O
S	T	O	O	P		T		Y		L		N

238

S	T	A	N	D	I	N	G			Y		I
H		U		O		A		R	H	E	U	M
I	N	S	O	L	E	N	C	E		A		P
R		T		L		T		L		S	E	E
E	V	E	N		R	E	C	A	N	T		D
		R		R		S		T				E
S	E	E	S	A	W		R	E	W	A	R	D
C				N		P		D		R		
R		R	A	S	C	A	L		E	B	B	S
A	D	O		A		N		B		I		Y
T		D		C	H	A	R	L	A	T	A	N
C	H	E	C	K		M		O		E		O
H		O			F	A	L	T	E	R	E	D

239

S	U	M	M	E	R			S	A	L	T	S
T		A		A		S		L		A		T
R	A	C	E	R		T	R	A	C	T	O	R
E		H		T		O		P		C		I
W	H	I	T	H	E	R			T	H	U	D
N		N		H		M	A	R				E
	V	E	T	O				E	A	S	Y	
P				G	A	P		P		C		A
A	P	S	E			L	O	A	T	H	E	D
S		T		H		A		R		E		D
T	O	R	R	E	N	T		T	A	M	I	L
E		U		S		E		E		E		E
L	O	T	U	S			H	E	E	D	E	D

240

A	L	L	E	Y			G	A	I	T	E	R
L		E		A		P		C		A		E
P	R	A	I	R	I	E		R	A	N	G	E
A		N		D		N		I		K		K
C	U	T	E			C	O	M	R	A	D	E
A				H	U	E		O		R		D
	G	A	L	A				N	O	D	E	
P		C		R		I	V	Y				W
A	C	C	L	A	I	M			S	T	A	Y
R		O		N		A		G		H		V
C	L	U	N	G		G	A	R	B	A	G	E
E		N		U		E		I		N		R
L	I	T	T	E	R			T	O	K	E	N